Acoustic Hits
Easy Guitar

CW00428714

Hal Leonard Europe
Distributed by Music Sales

Exclusive Distributors:
Music Sales Limited
8-9 Frith Street, London W1V 5TZ, England.
Music Sales Pty Limited
120 Rothschild Avenue, Rosebery, NSW 2018, Australia.

Order No. HLE90000440
ISBN 0-7119-6902-7
This book © Copyright 1998 by Hal Leonard Europe

Cover design by Pearce Marchbank, Studio Twenty, London

Printed in the United States of America.

Your Guarantee of Quality
As publishers, we strive to produce every
book to the highest commercial standards.
This book has been carefully designed to minimise
awkward page turns and to make playing from it a real pleasure.
Throughout, the printing and binding have been planned to ensure a sturdy,
attractive publication which should give years of enjoyment.
If your copy fails to meet our high standards, please inform us and
we will gladly replace it.

Music Sales' complete catalogue describes thousands of titles and is
available in full colour sections by subject, direct from Music Sales Limited.
Please state your areas of interest and send a cheque/postal order for £1.50 for postage to:
Music Sales Limited, Newmarket Road, Bury St. Edmunds,
Suffolk IP33 3YB, England.

Visit the Internet Music Shop at
http://www.musicsales.co.uk

STRUM AND PICK PATTERNS

This chart contains the suggested strum and pick patterns that are referred to by number at the beginning of each song in this book. The symbols ⊓ and ∨ in the strum patterns refer to down and up strokes, respectively. The letters in the pick patterns indicate which right-hand fingers plays which strings.

p = thumb
i = index finger
m = middle finger
a = ring finger

For example; Pick Pattern 2
is played: thumb - index - middle - ring

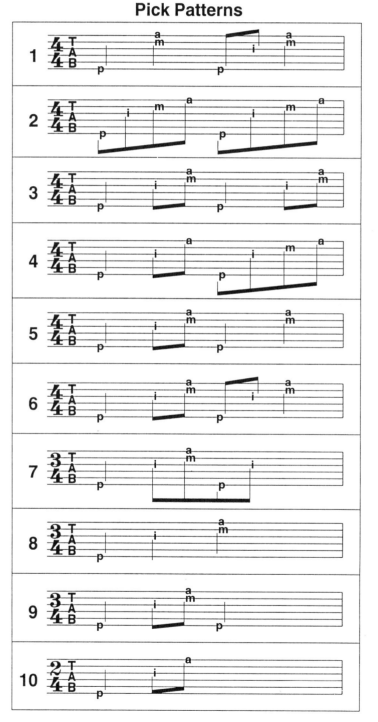

Strum Patterns   ## Pick Patterns

You can use the 3/4 Strum or Pick Patterns in songs written in compound meter (6/8, 9/8, 12/8, etc.).
For example, you can accompany a song in 6/8 by playing the 3/4 pattern twice in each measure.
The 4/4 Strum and Pick Patterns can be used for songs written in cut time (¢) by doubling the note time values in the patterns. Each pattern would therefore last two measures in cut time.

Blackbird

Words and Music by John Lennon and Paul McCartney

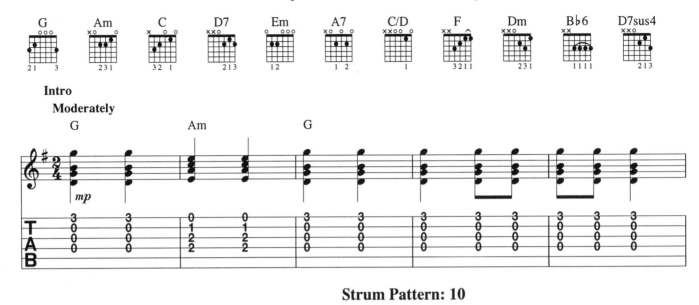

Intro
Moderately

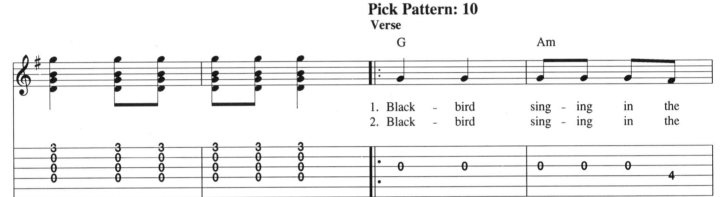

Strum Pattern: 10
Pick Pattern: 10
Verse

1. Black - bird sing - ing in the
2. Black - bird sing - ing in the

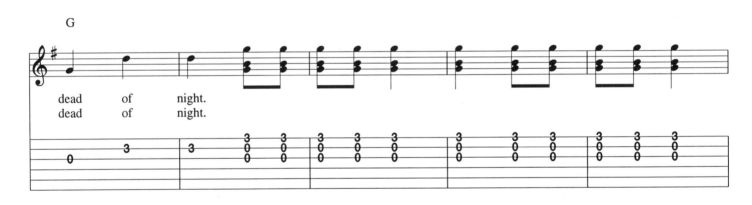

dead of night.
dead of night.

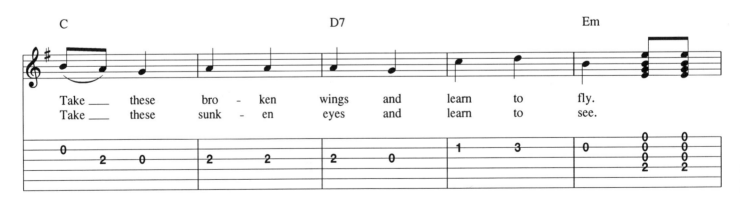

Take ___ these bro - ken wings and learn to fly.
Take ___ these sunk - en eyes and learn to see.

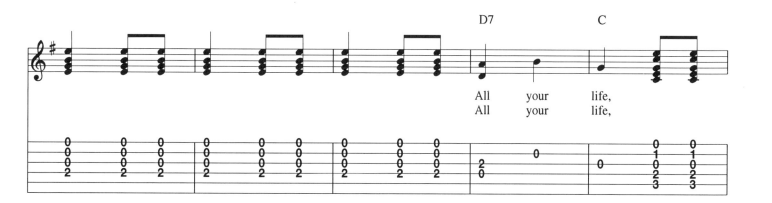

All your life,
All your life,

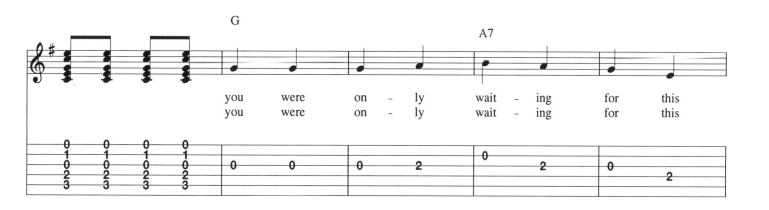

you were on – ly wait – ing for this
you were on – ly wait – ing for this

1.

mo – ment to a – rise.
mo – ment

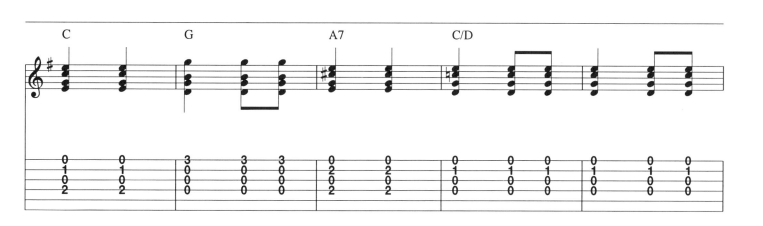

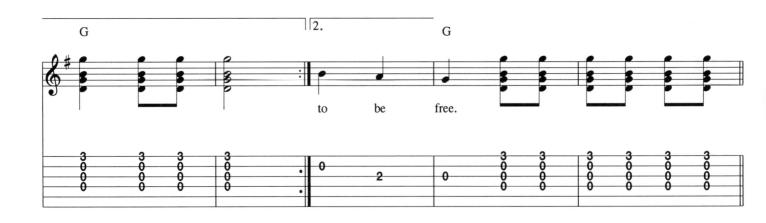

to be free.

Chorus

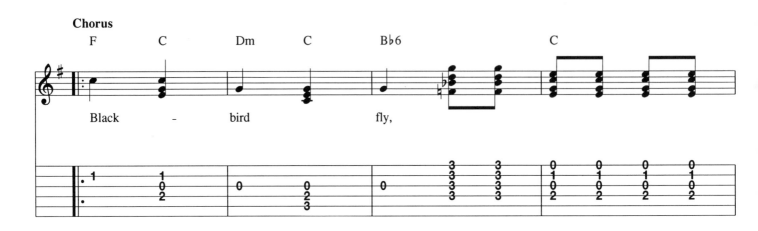

Black - bird fly,

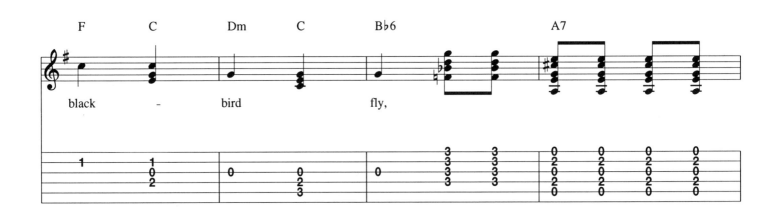

black - bird fly,

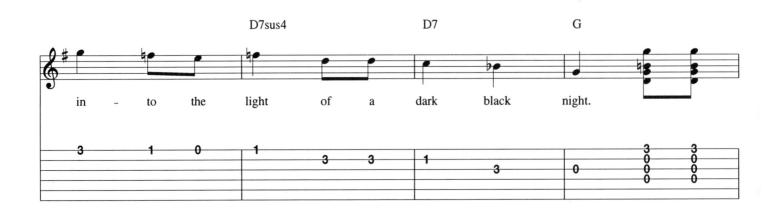

in - to the light of a dark black night.

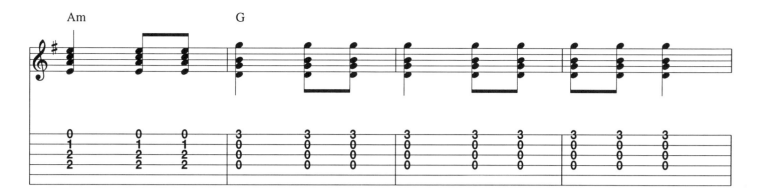

Verse

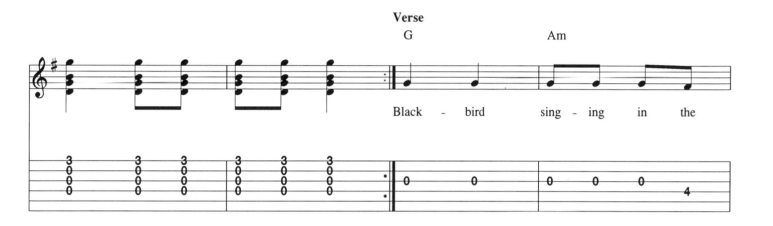

Black - bird sing - ing in the

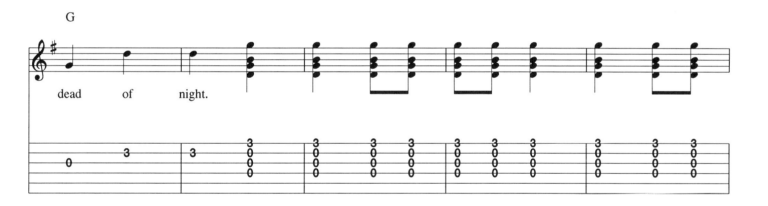

dead of night.

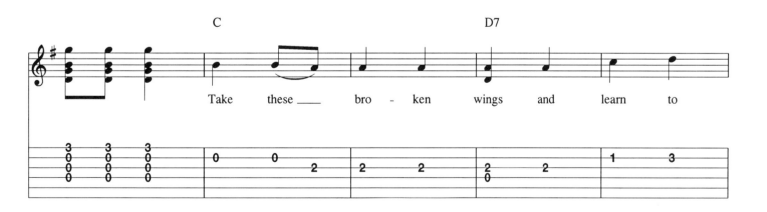

Take these ___ bro - ken wings and learn to

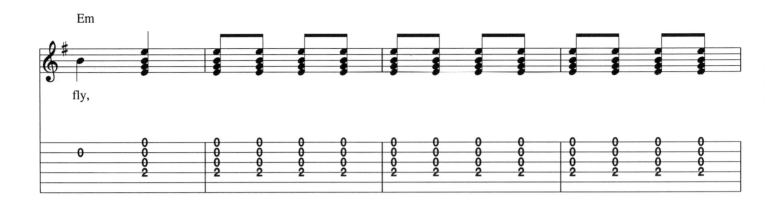

Em

fly,

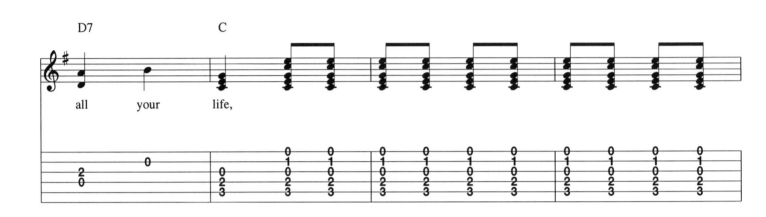

D7   C

all   your   life,

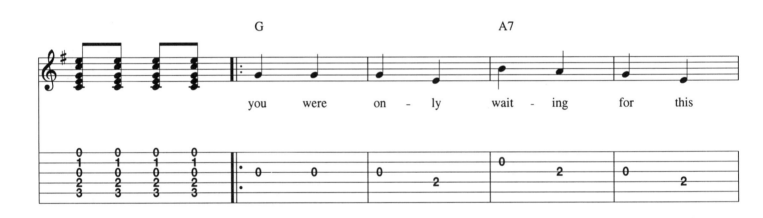

G   A7

you   were   on - ly   wait - ing   for   this

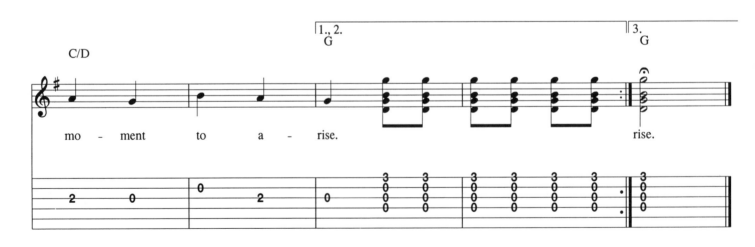

C/D

1., 2.
G

3.
G

mo - ment   to   a - rise.   rise.

Blaze Of Glory

Words and Music by Jon Bon Jovi

Strum Pattern: 2
Pick Pattern: 6

Intro
Moderately

1. Wake up in the morn - ing, and I raise my wea - ry head.

I've got an old coat for a pil - low, and the earth was last night's

bed. I don't know where I'm go - ing, on - ly God knows where I've

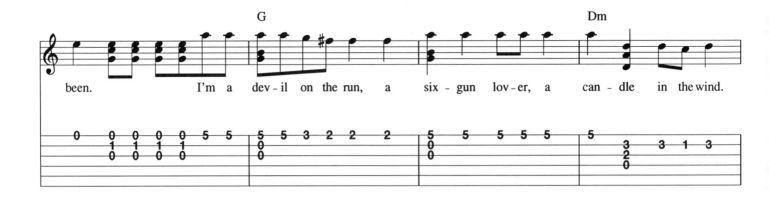

been.   I'm a dev-il on the run,   a   six-gun lov-er, a   can-dle   in the wind.

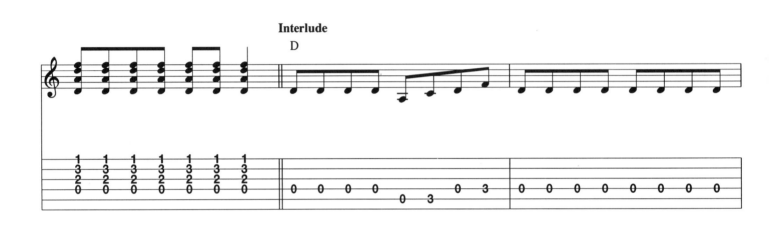

Interlude

Verse

2. When you're brought in - to   this   world, __   they
   ask   a - bout   my   con-science, and   I

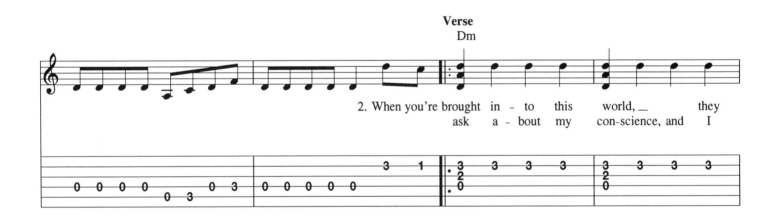

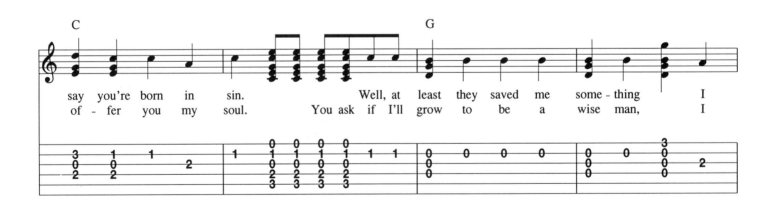

say   you're   born   in   sin.   Well, at   least   they   saved   me   some-thing   I
of - fer   you   my   soul.   You ask if I'll   grow   to   be   a   wise man,   I

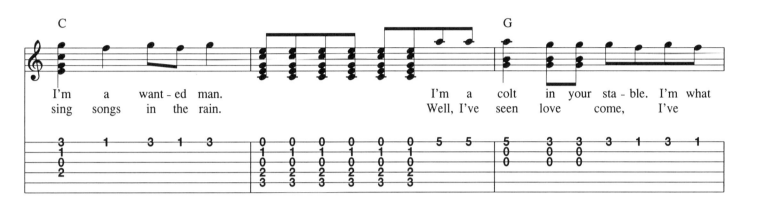

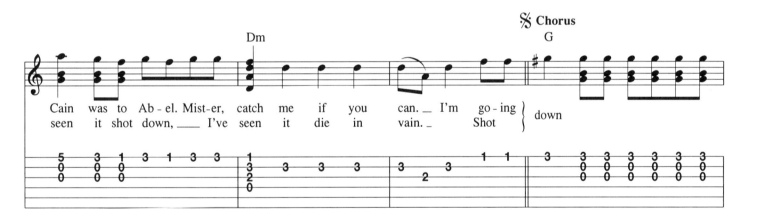

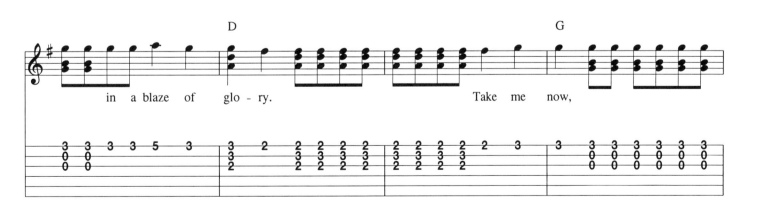

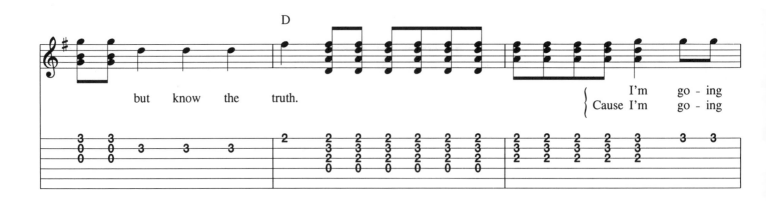

but know the truth.

I'm go - ing
Cause I'm go - ing

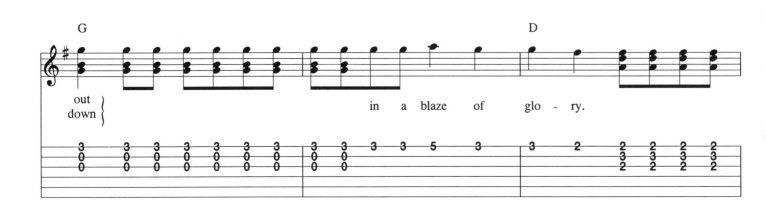

out
down

in a blaze of glo - ry.

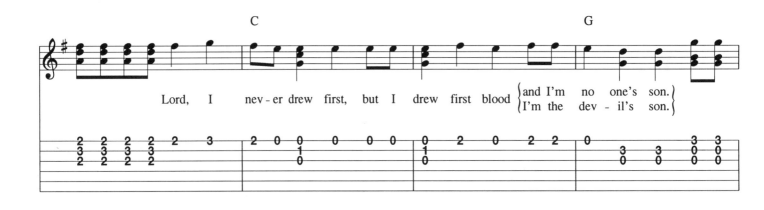

Lord, I nev - er drew first, but I drew first blood
and I'm no one's son.
I'm the dev - il's son.

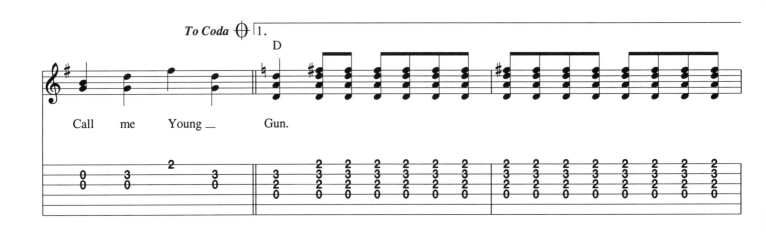

To Coda $\oplus$ 1.

Call me Young __ Gun.

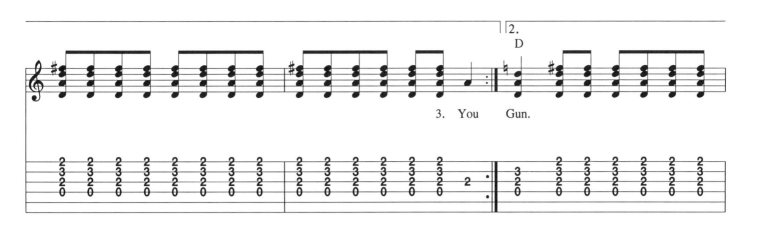

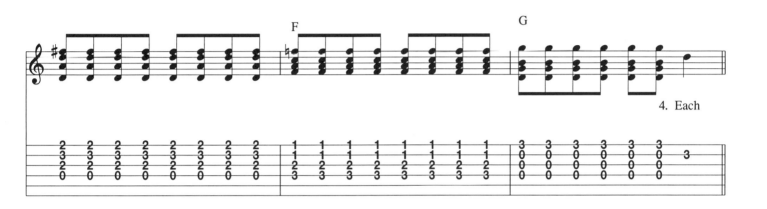

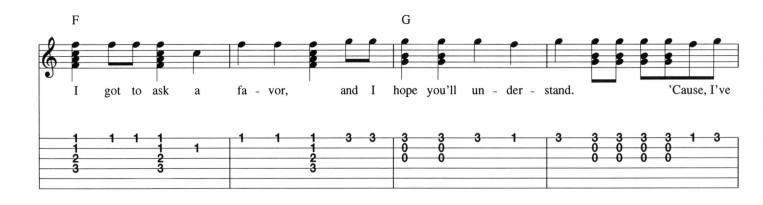

I got to ask a fa - vor, and I hope you'll un - der - stand. 'Cause, I've

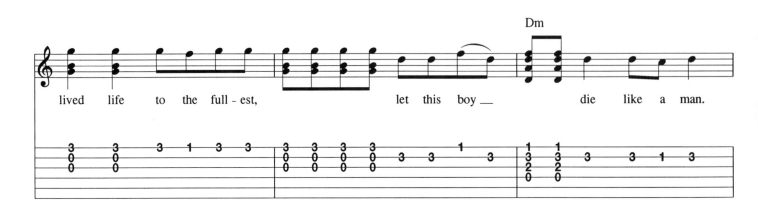

lived life to the full - est, let this boy ___ die like a man.

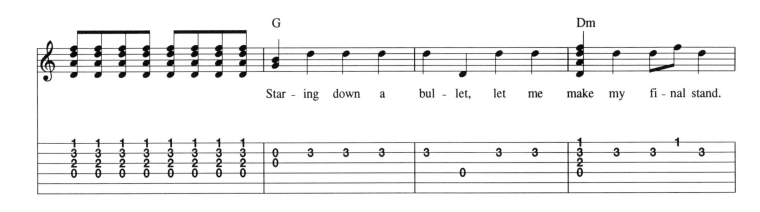

Star - ing down a bul - let, let me make my fi - nal stand.

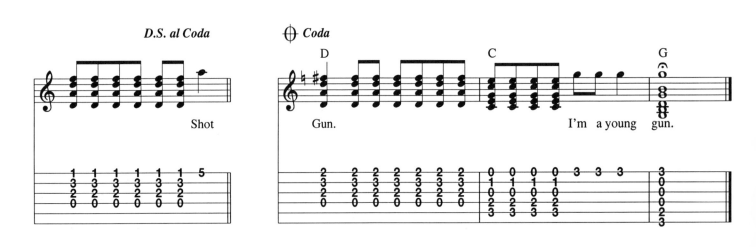

Shot Gun. I'm a young gun.

Change the World

featured on the Motion Picture Soundtrack PHENOMENON

Words and Music by Gordon Kennedy, Tommy Sims and Wayne Kirkpatrick

Strum Pattern: 3
Pick Pattern: 4

15

%S Chorus

it's on-ly in my dreams ___ that I can change ___ the

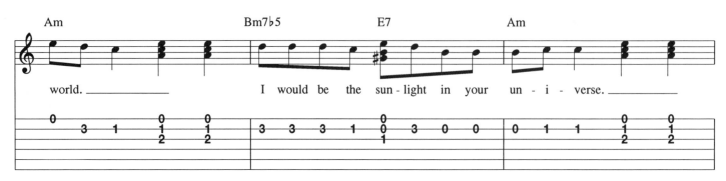

world. ___ I would be the sun-light in your un-i-verse. ___

To Coda ⊕

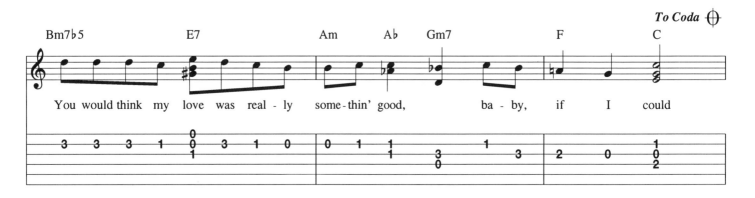

You would think my love was real-ly some-thin' good, ba-by, if I could

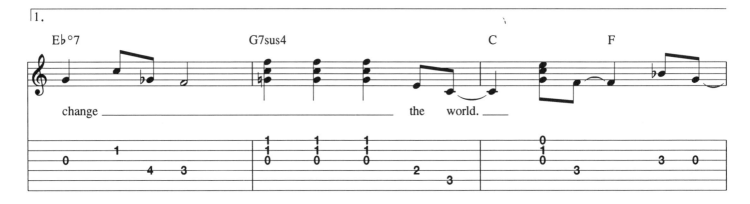

change ___ the world. ___

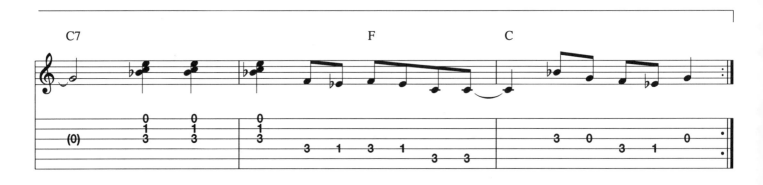

D.S. al Coda

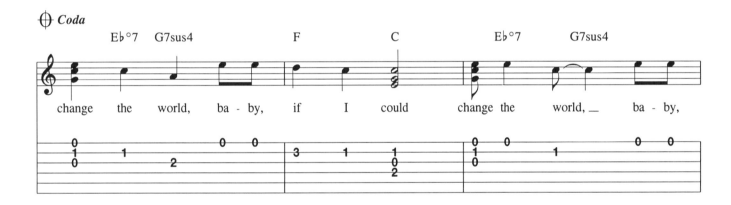

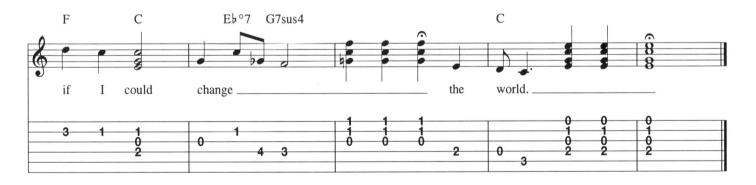

Additional Lyrics

2. If I could be king
   Even for a day,
   I'd take you as my queen,
   I'd have it no other way.
   And our love would rule
   In this kingdom that we had made
   Till then I'll be a fool,
   Wishin' for the day...

Don't Look Back in Anger

Words and Music by Noel Gallagher

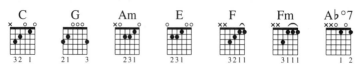

Strum Pattern: 4
Pick Pattern: 1

Verse
Moderately

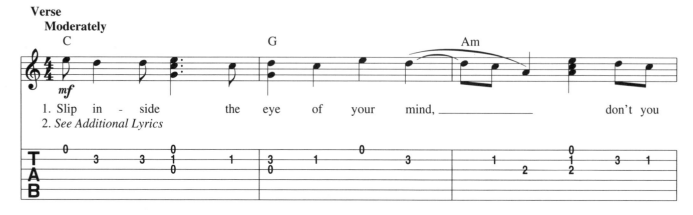

1. Slip in - side the eye of your mind, _____ don't you
2. *See Additional Lyrics*

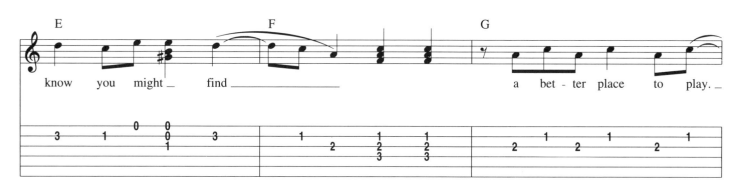

know you might __ find _____ a bet - ter place to play. __

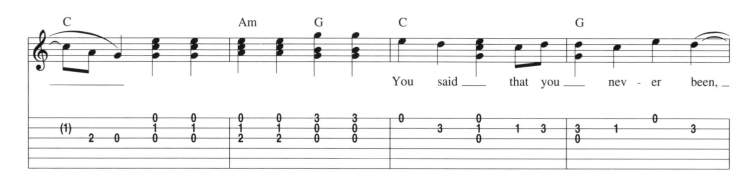

You said ___ that you ___ nev - er been, __

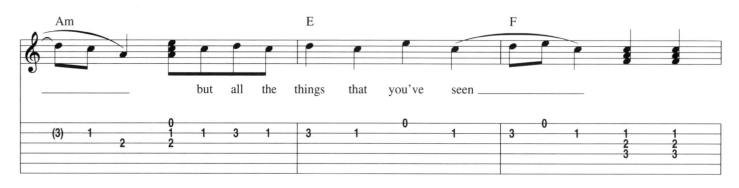

but all the things that you've seen _____

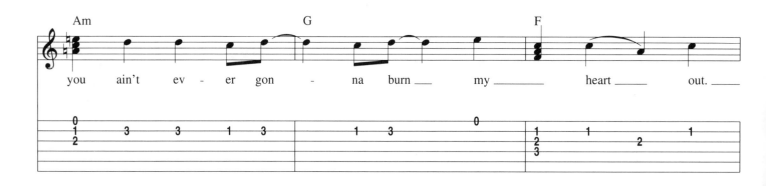

you ain't ev - er gon - na burn ___ my _____ heart _____ out. ____

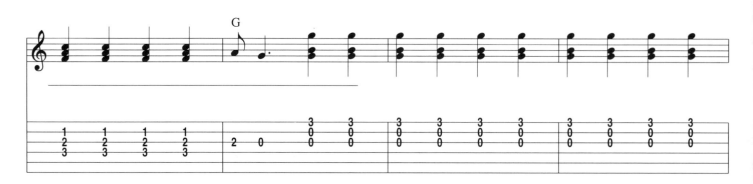

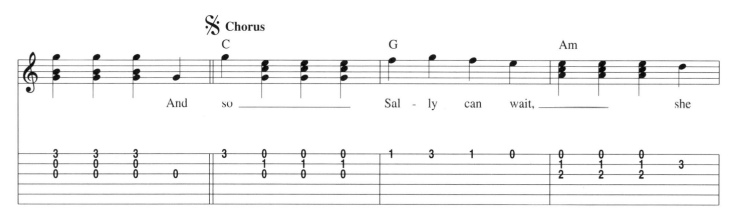

𝄋 **Chorus**

And so _____ Sal - ly can wait, _____ she

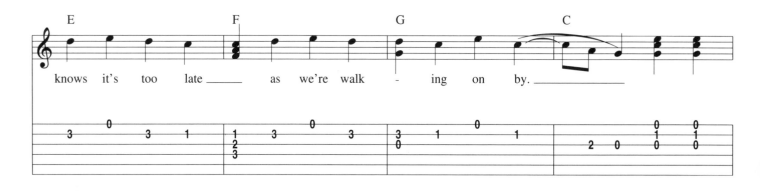

knows it's too late _____ as we're walk - ing on by. _____

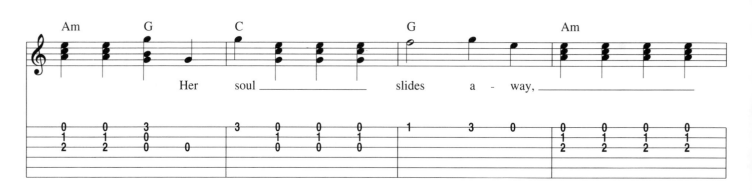

Her soul _____ slides a - way, _____

Additional Lyrics

2. Take me to the place where you go
   Where nobody knows if it's night or day
   But please don't put your life in the hands
   Of a rock 'n' roll band who'll throw it all away.

Pre-Chorus I'm gonna start a revolution from my bed
   'Cause you said the brains I had went to my head.
   Step outside 'cause summertime's in bloom.
   Stand up beside the fireplace, take that look from your face
   'Cause you ain't never gonna burn my heart out.

Free Bird

Words and Music by Allen Collins and Ronnie Van Zant

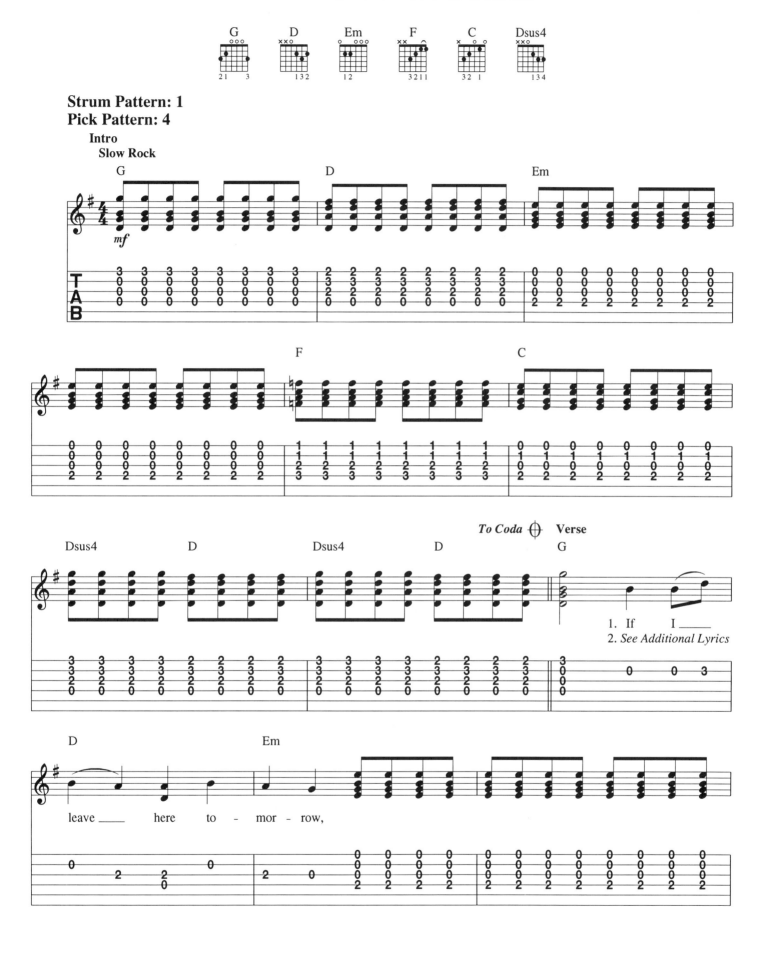

Strum Pattern: 1
Pick Pattern: 4

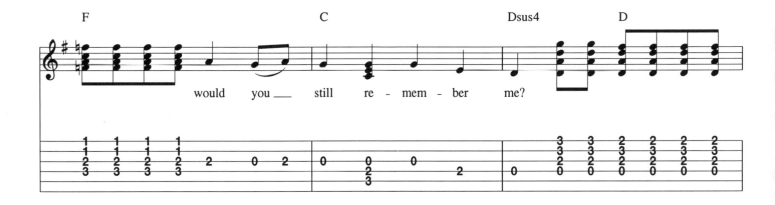

would you __ still re-mem-ber me?

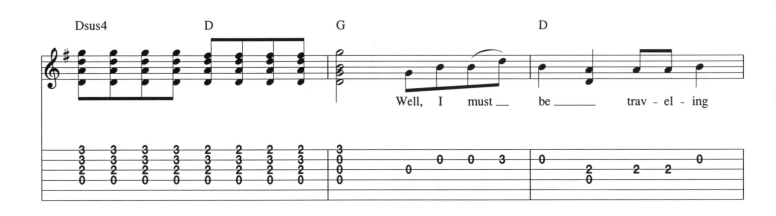

Well, I must __ be __ trav-el-ing

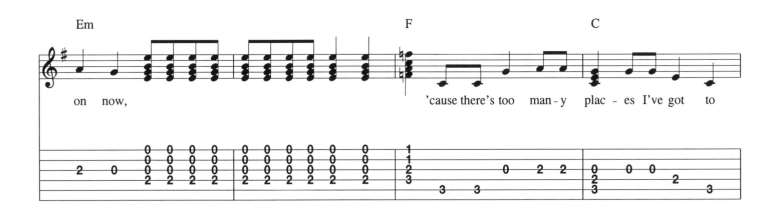

on now, 'cause there's too man-y plac-es I've got to

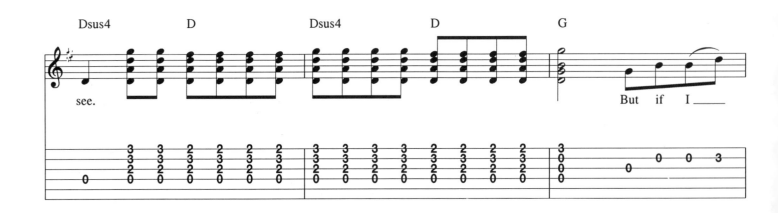

see. But if I ____

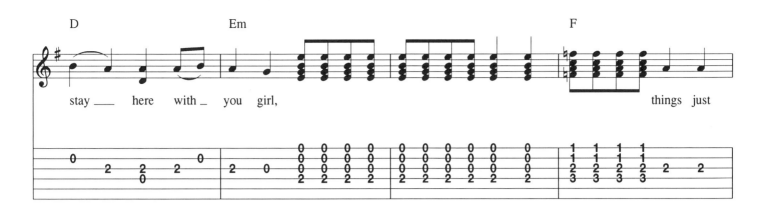

stay ___ here with ___ you girl,   things just

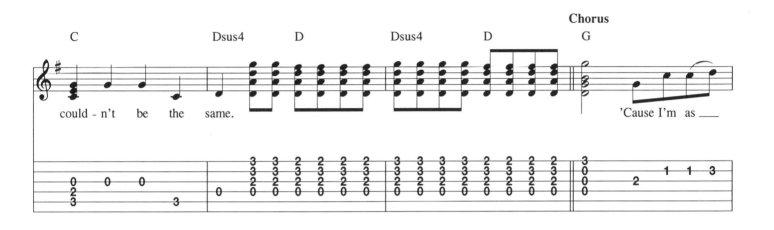

could - n't be the same.   **Chorus**   'Cause I'm as ___

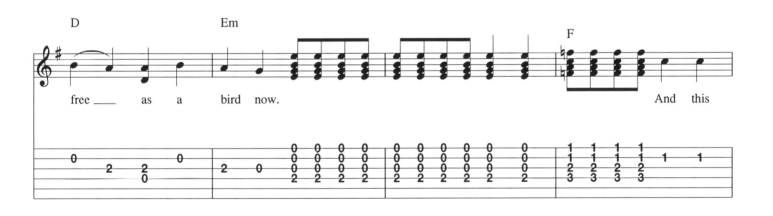

free ___ as a bird now.   And this

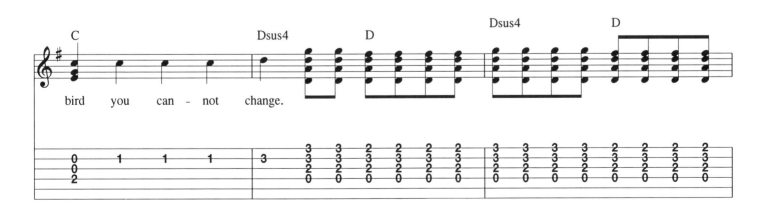

bird you can - not change.

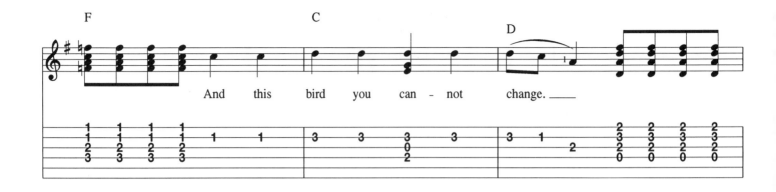

And this bird you can-not change. _____

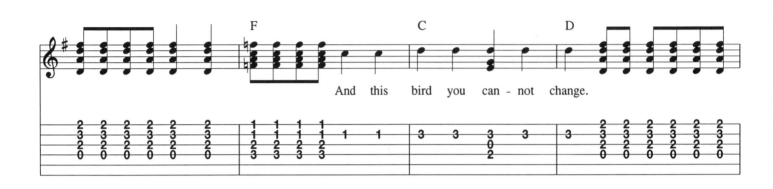

And this bird you can-not change.

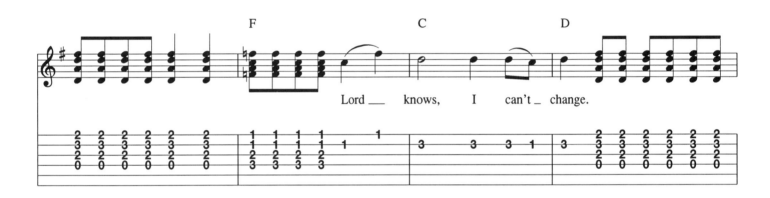

Lord _____ knows, I can't _ change.

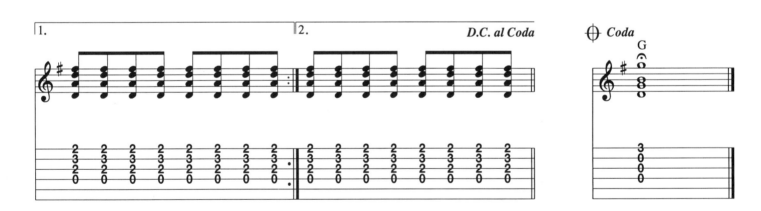

Additonal Lyrics

2. Bye, bye baby, it's been sweet now, yeah, yeah,
   Though this feelin' I can't change.
   A please don't take it so badly,
   'Cause the Lord knows I'm to blame.
   But if I stay here with you girl,
   Things just couldn't be the same.

Ironic

Lyrics by Alanis Morissette
Music by Alanis Morissette and Glen Ballard

Strum Pattern: 2
Pick Pattern: 4

Intro

Moderate Rock

MCA music publishing

27

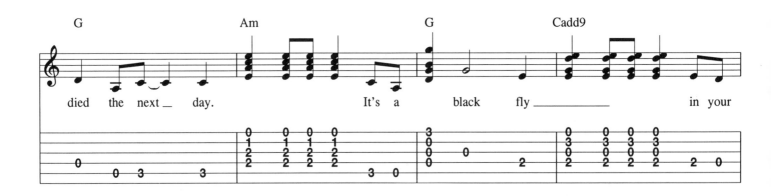

To Coda ⊕

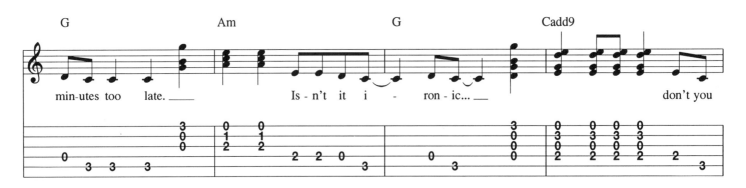

Chorus

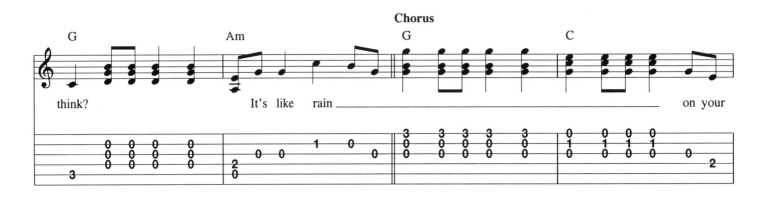

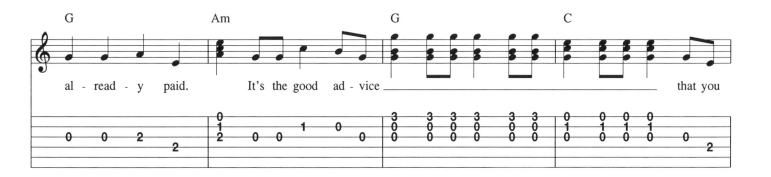

al - read - y paid. It's the good ad - vice _____ that you

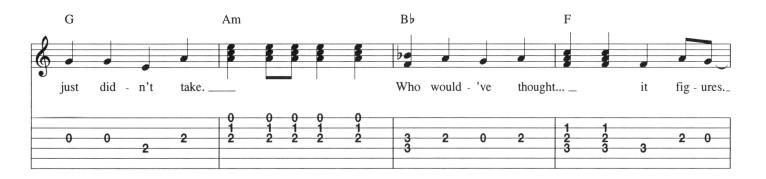

just did - n't take. ___ Who would - 've thought... _ it fig - ures._

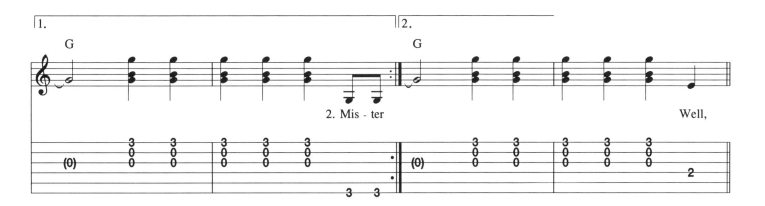

2. Mis - ter

Well,

Bridge

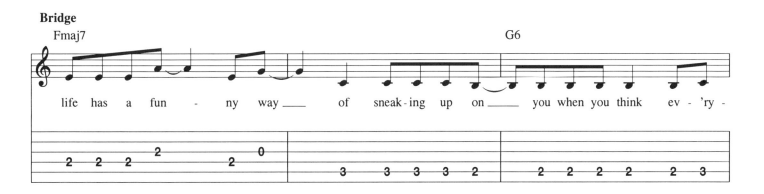

life has a fun - ny way ___ of sneak - ing up on ___ you when you think ev - 'ry-

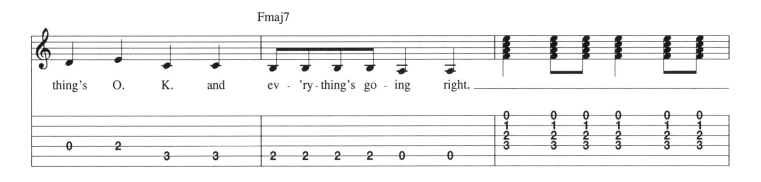

thing's O. K. and ev - 'ry - thing's go - ing right. _____

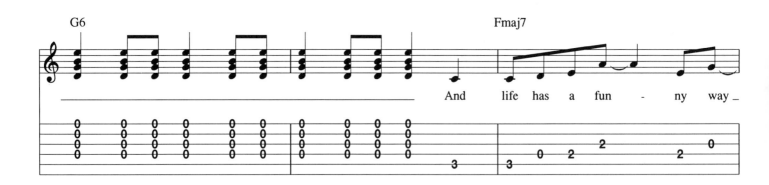

And life has a fun - ny way

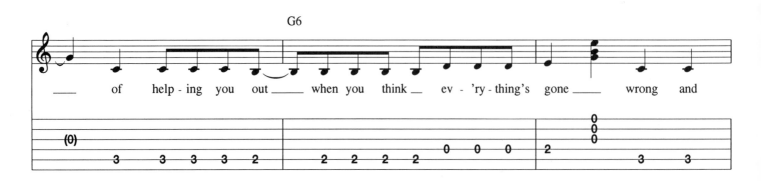

of help - ing you out ____ when you think ____ ev - 'ry - thing's gone ____ wrong and

D.S. al Coda

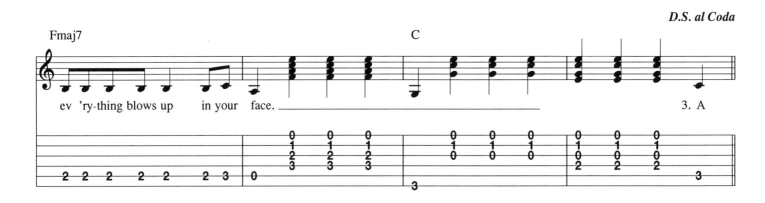

ev - 'ry - thing blows up in your face. _____ 3. A

Coda

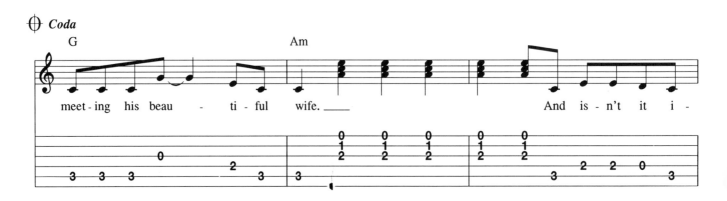

meet - ing his beau - ti - ful wife. ____ And is - n't it i -

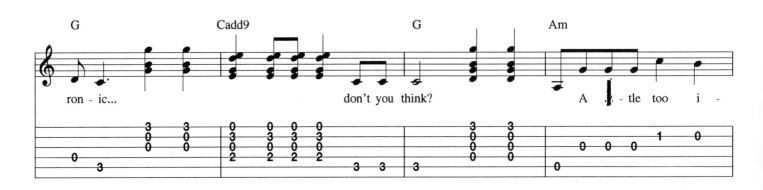

ron - ic... don't you think? A lit - tle too i -

ron - ic...   and yeah, I real - ly do think...   it's like rain

Chorus

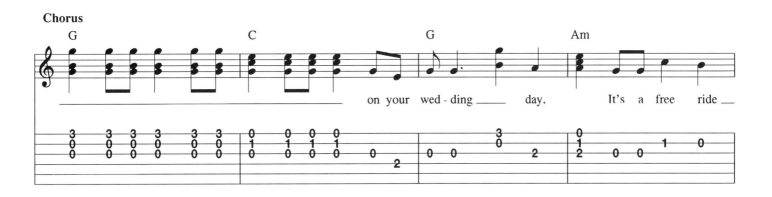

on your wed - ding _____ day,   It's a free ride _____

when you're al - read - y paid.   It's the good ad-vice_

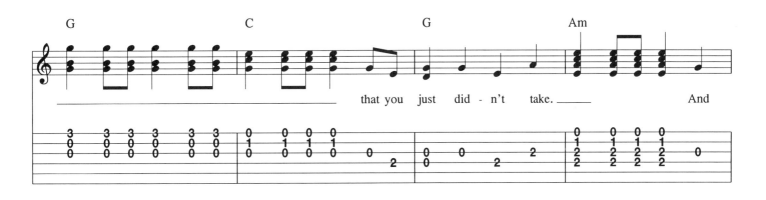

that you just did - n't take. _____   And

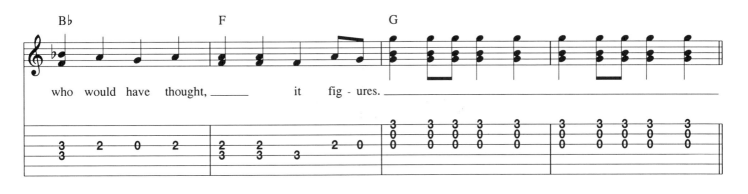

who would have thought, _____ it fig - ures. _____

Outro

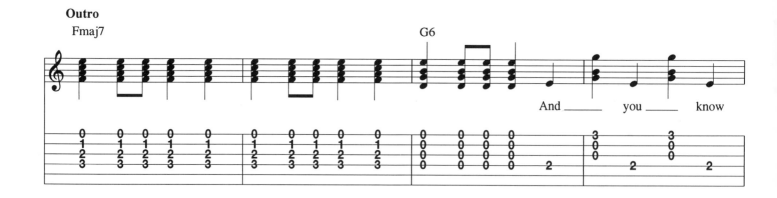

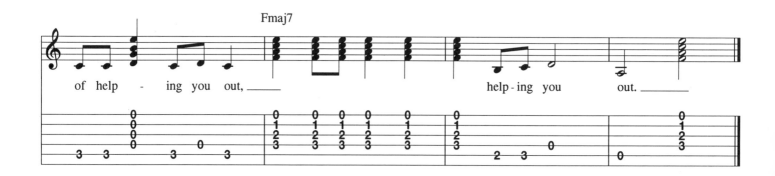

Additional Lyrics

2. Mister Play It Safe was afraid to fly.
   He packed his suitcase and kissed his kids goodbye.
   He waited his whole damn life to take that flight,
   And as the plane crashed down, he thought, "Well, isn't this nice..."

3. A traffic jam when you're already late.
   A no smoking sign on your cigarette break.
   It's like ten thousand spoons when all you need is a knife.
   It's meeting the man of my dreams, and then meeting his beautiful wife.

Layla

Words and Music by Eric Clapton and Jim Gordon

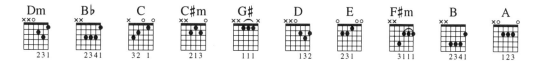

Strum Pattern: 3
Pick Pattern: 3

Intro
Moderately Slow

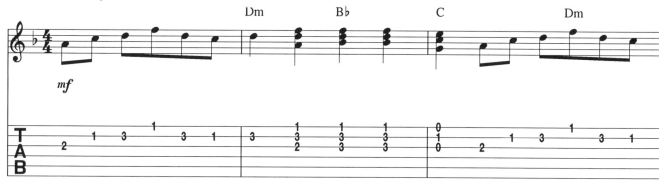

1. What-'ll you do when you get lone-ly
2. Tried   to give you con-so-la-tion;
3. Let's make the best of the sit-u-a-tion

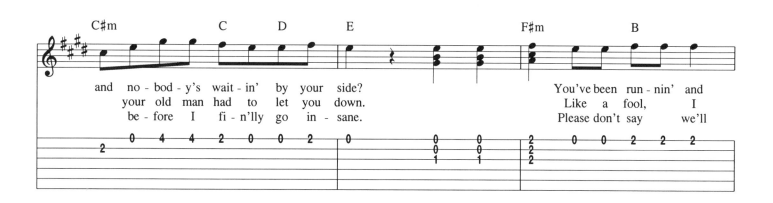

and no-bod-y's wait-in' by your side?
your old man had to let you down.
be-fore I fi-n'lly go in-sane.

You've been run-nin' and
Like a fool, I
Please don't say we'll

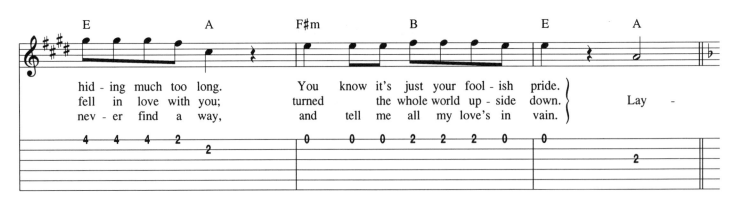

hid - ing much too long.
fell in love with you;
nev - er find a way,

You know it's just your fool - ish pride.
turned the whole world up - side down.
and tell me all my love's in vain.

Lay -

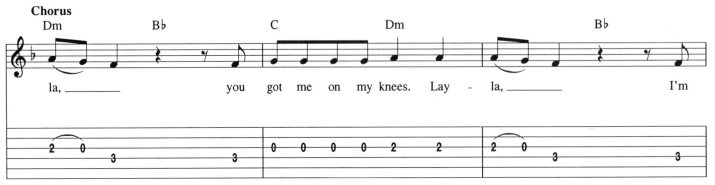

Chorus

la, _____ you got me on my knees. Lay - la, _____ I'm

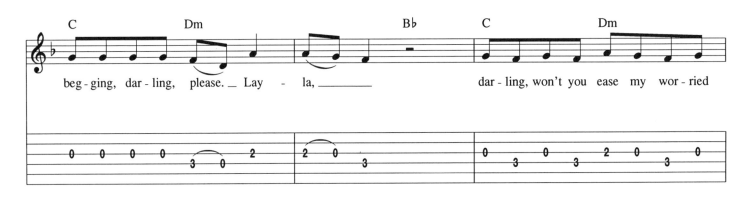

beg - ging, dar - ling, please. _ Lay - la, _____ dar - ling, won't you ease my wor - ried

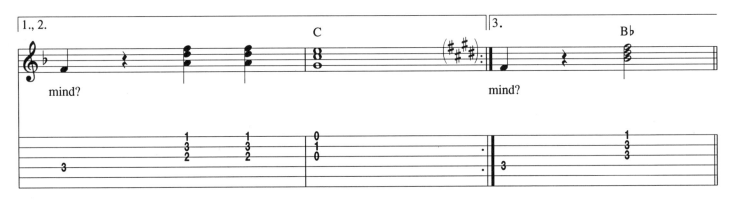

1., 2.

mind?

3.

mind?

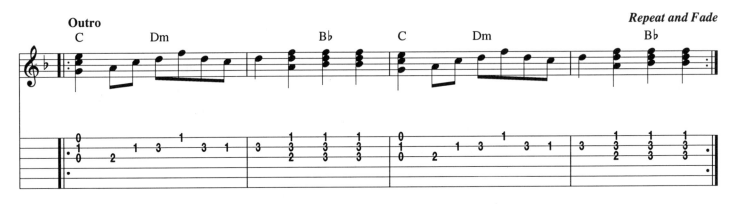

Repeat and Fade

Outro

Love Song

Words and Music by Jeffrey Keith and Frank Hannon

Strum Pattern: 2, 4
Pick Pattern: 2, 4

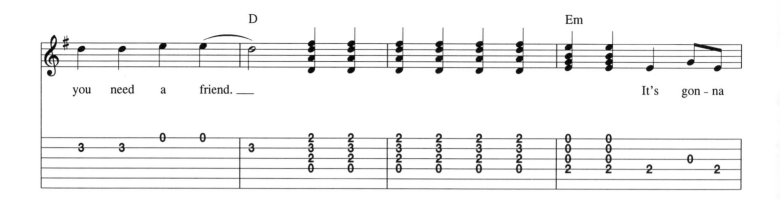

you need a friend. ___   It's gon - na

take a lit - tle time. _____   I know.   Time is sure

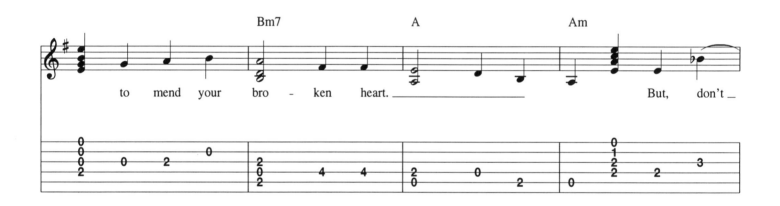

to mend your bro - ken heart. _____   But, don't _

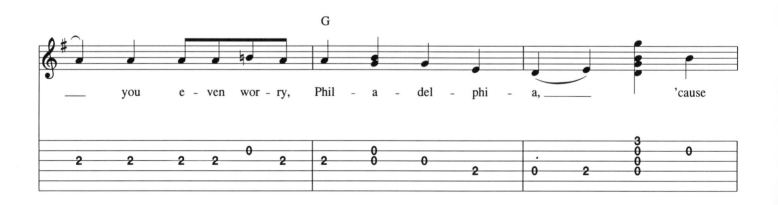

___ you e - ven wor - ry, Phil - a - del - phi - a, _____   'cause

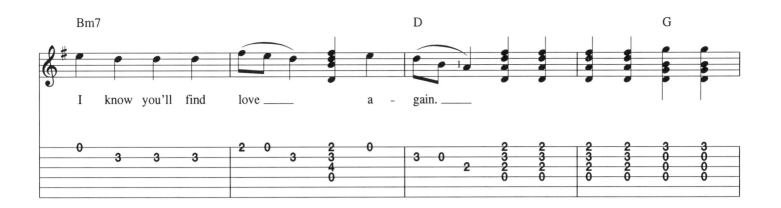

I know you'll find love ____ a - gain. ____

New York. Ooh, yeah. ____

Chorus

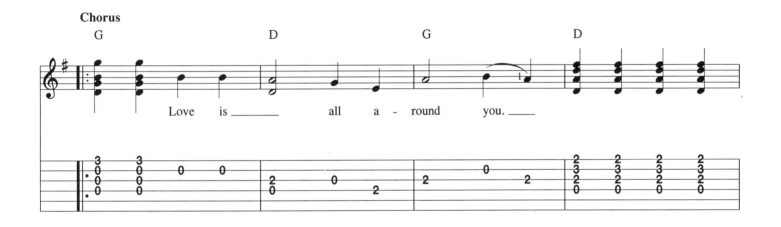

Love is ____ all a - round you. ____

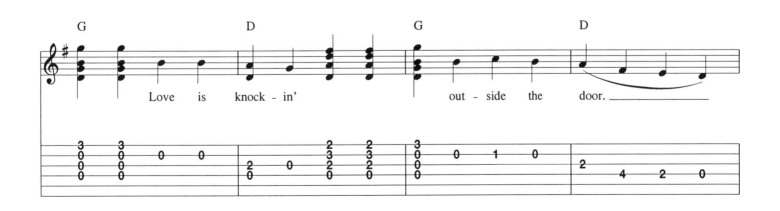

Love is knock - in' out - side the door. ____

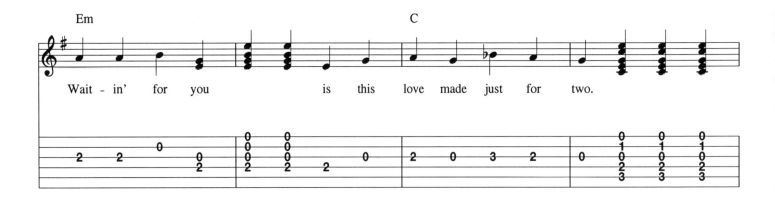

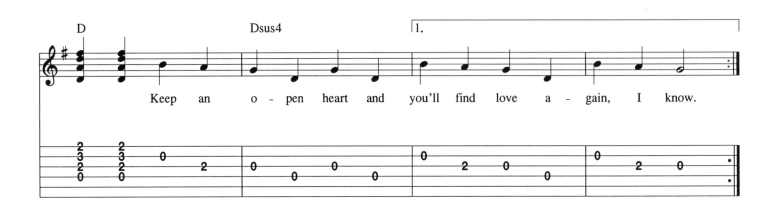

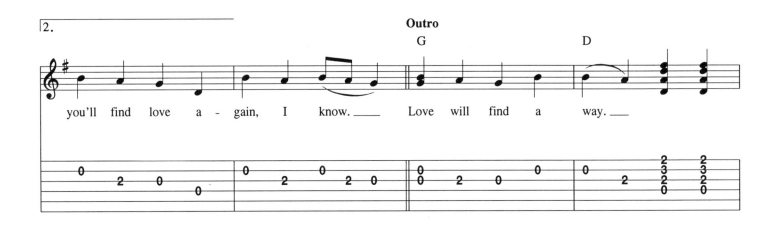

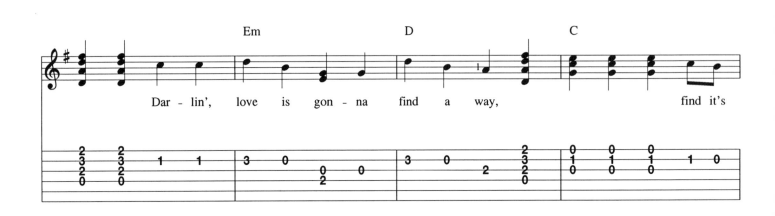

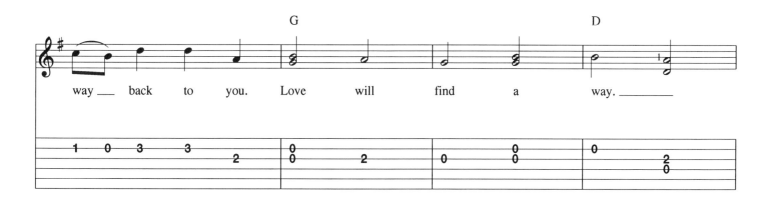

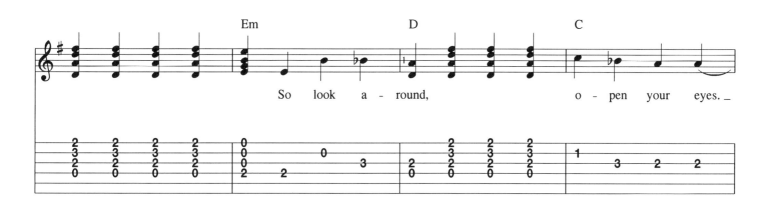

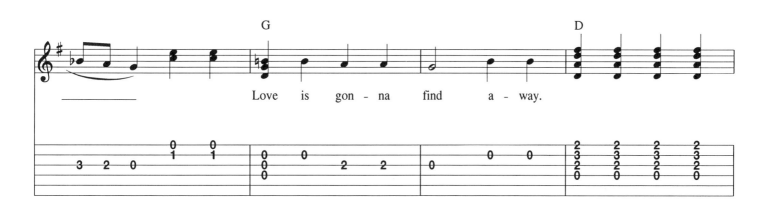

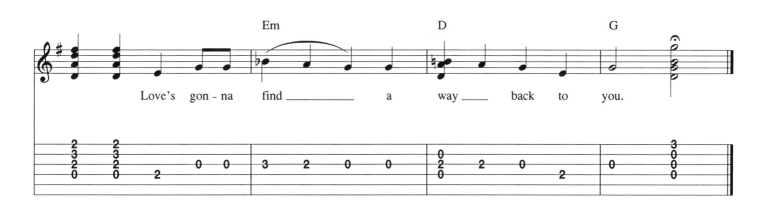

My Friends

Words and Music by Anthony Kiedis, Michael Balzary, Chad Smith and David Navarro

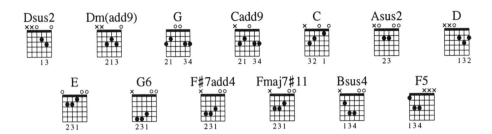

Strum Pattern: 1
Pick Pattern: 2

Intro

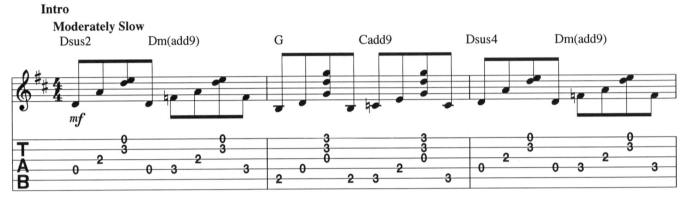

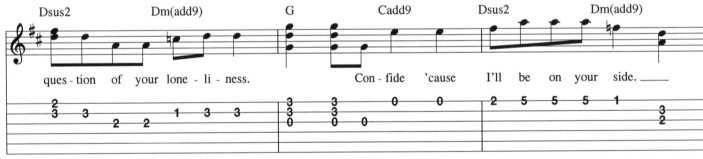

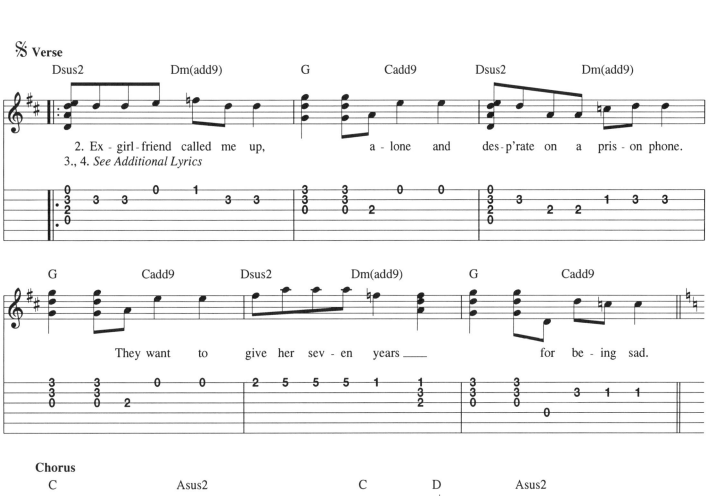

Verse

2. Ex-girl-friend called me up,   a-lone and des-p'rate on a pris-on phone.
3., 4. *See Additional Lyrics*

They want to give her sev-en years _____ for be-ing sad.

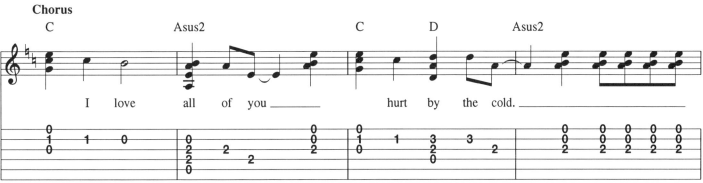

Chorus

I love all of you _____ hurt by the cold. _____

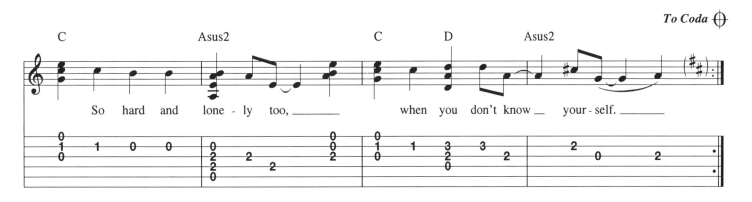

To Coda ⊕

So hard and lone-ly too, _____ when you don't know _____ your-self. _____

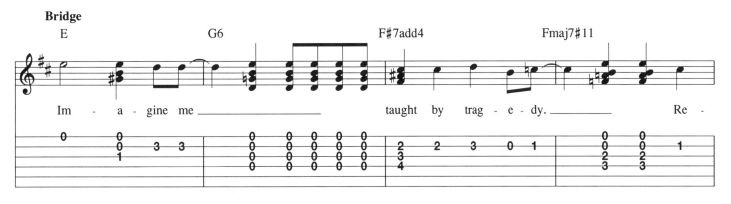

Bridge

Im-a-gine me _____ taught by trag-e-dy. _____ Re-

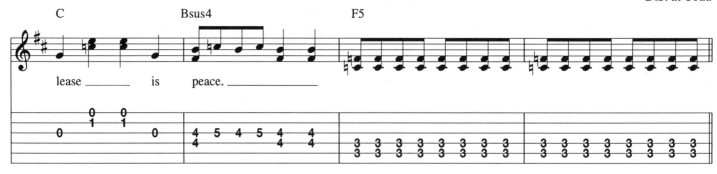

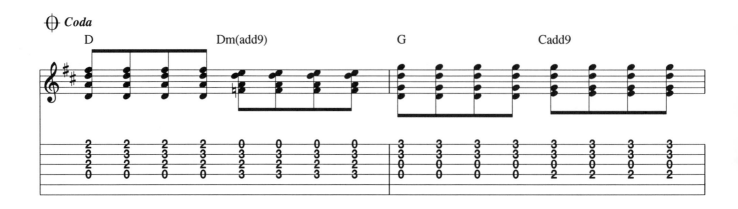

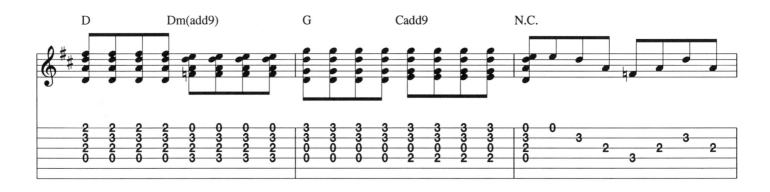

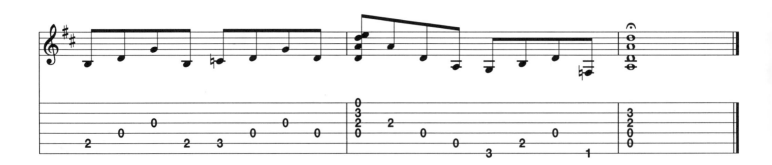

Additional Lyrics

3. My friends are so distressed.
   They're standing on the brink of emptiness.
   No words, I know what to express, this emptiness.

4. I heard a little girl
   And what she said was something beautiful.
   To give your love no matter what is what she said.

Patience

Words and Music by W. Axl Rose, Slash, Izzy Stradlin', Duff McKagan and Steven Adler

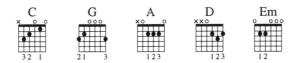

Strum Pattern: 3
Pick Pattern: 3

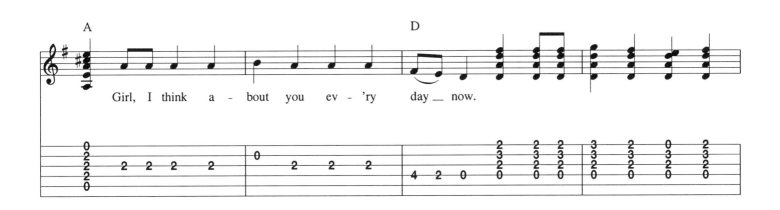

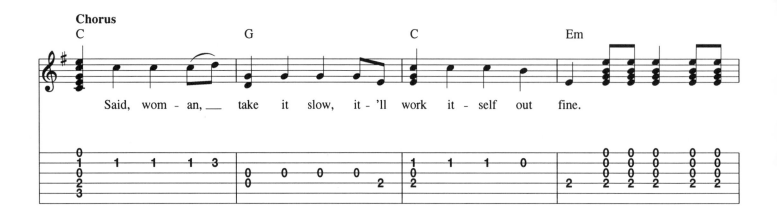

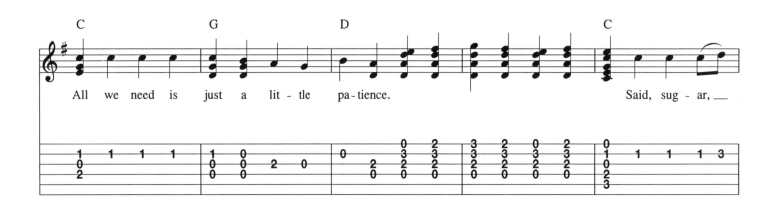

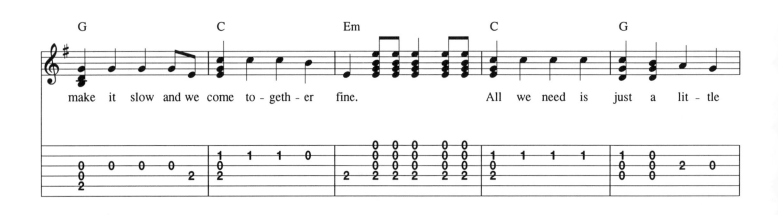

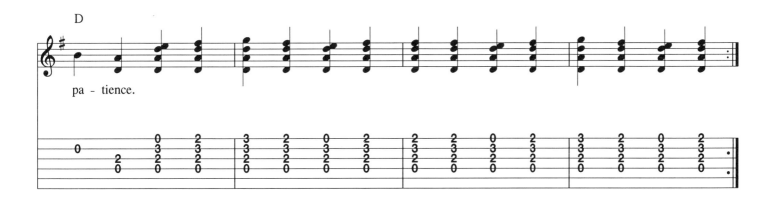

pa - tience.

Outro

Repeat and Fade

D   G

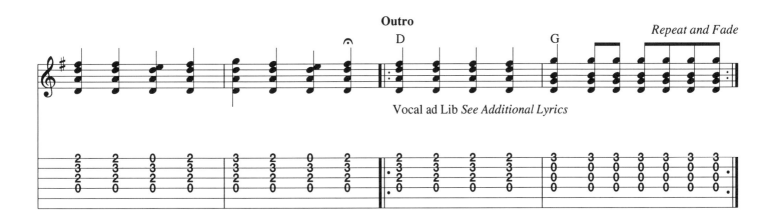

Vocal ad Lib *See Additional Lyrics*

Additional Lyrics

2. I sit here on the stairs 'cause I'd rather be alone.
   If I can't have you right now I'll wait, dear.
   Sometimes I get so tense but I can't speed up the time.
   But you know, love, there's one more thing to consider.
   Said, woman, take it slow and things will be just fine.
   You and I'll just use a little patience.
   Said, sugar, take the time 'cause the lights are shining bright.
   You and I've got what it takes to make it.
   We won't fake it, ah, I'll never break it 'cause I can't take it.

Vocal ad Lib.

Little patience, mm, yeah, mm, yeah,
Need a little patience, yeah.
Just a little patience, yeah.
Some more patience,
I been walkin' the streets at night
Just tryin' to get it right.
Hard to see with so many around.
You know I don't like being stuck in the ground,
And the streets don't change, but baby the name.
I ain't got time for the game 'cause I need you.
Yeah, yeah, but I need you, do, I need you.
Whoa I need you, oo, this time.

Running On Faith

Words and Music by Jerry Williams

Strum Pattern: 4
Pick Pattern: 5

Ballad ♩ = 65

Lately I been runnin' on faith. What else can a poor boy
Lately I been talk-in' in my sleep. Can't i-ma-gine what I'd have to
Then we'd go run-nin' on faith. All of our dreams will come

do? But my world will be right, when loves comes o-ver
say 'cept my world will be right, if love comes back my
true, and our world will be right, love comes o-ver

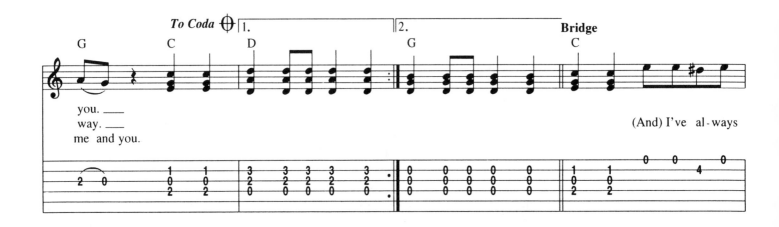

you. ___
way. ___
me and you.

(And) I've al-ways

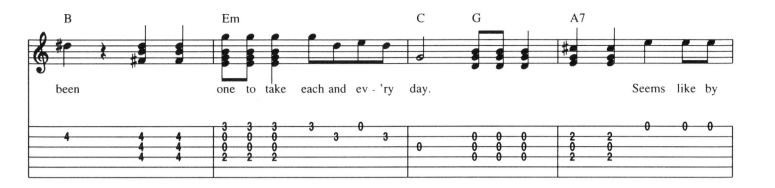

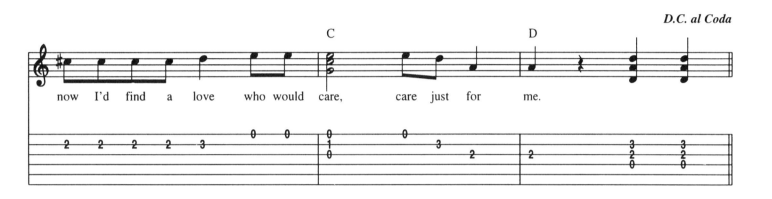

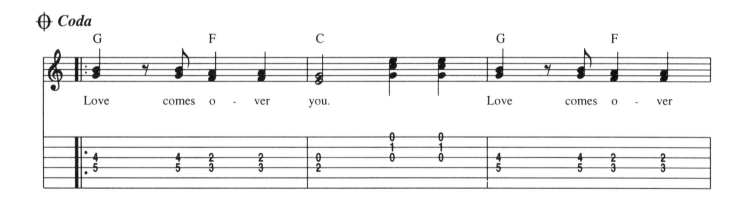

Tears in Heaven

Featured in the Motion Picture RUSH

Words and Music by Eric Clapton and Will Jennings

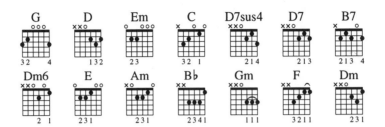

Strum Pattern: 6
Pick Pattern: 4

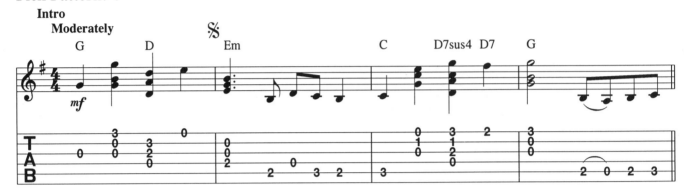

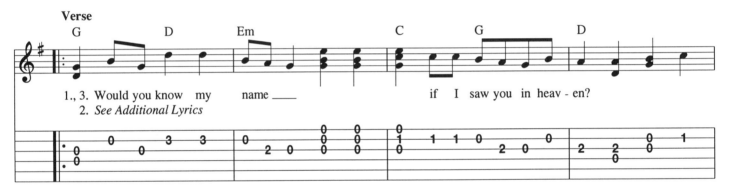

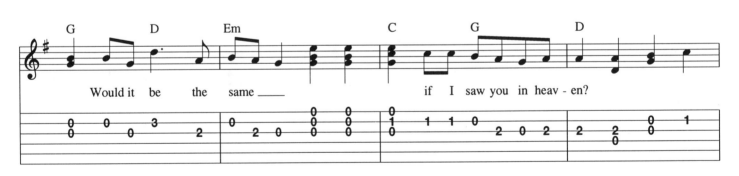

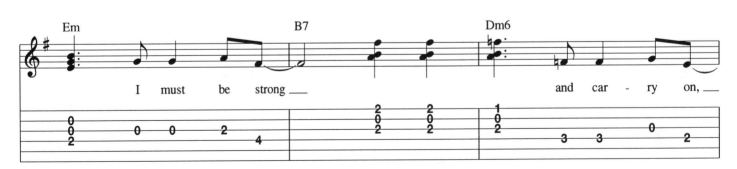

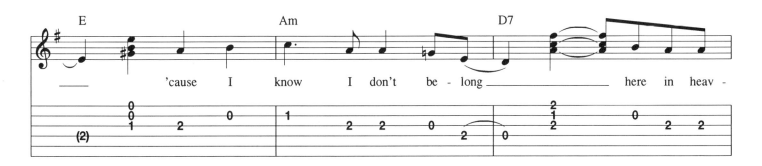

'cause I know I don't be - long _____ here in heav -

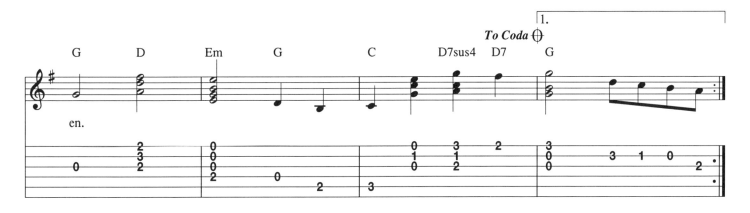

en.

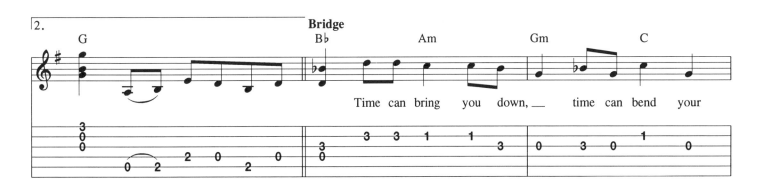

Time can bring you down, ___ time can bend your

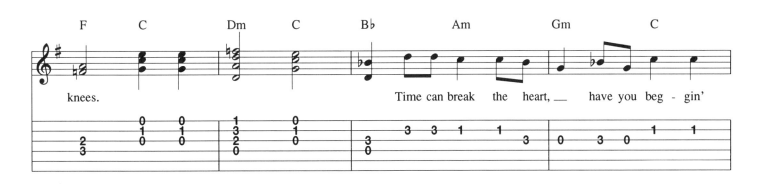

knees. Time can break the heart, ___ have you beg - gin'

please, _____ beg-gin' please. __

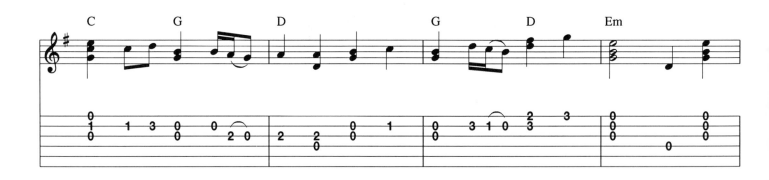

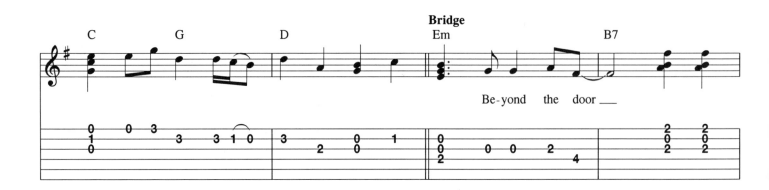

Be-yond   the   door ___

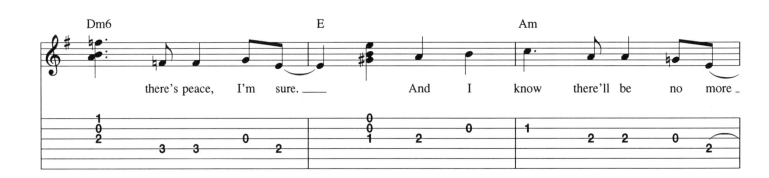

there's peace,   I'm   sure. ___   And   I   know   there'll be   no   more ___

D.S. al Coda

⊕ Coda

___   tears in heav - en. ___

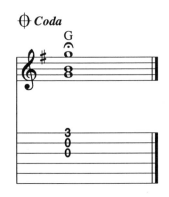

Additional Lyrics

2. Would you hold my hand
   If I saw you in heaven?
   Would you help me stand
   If I saw you in heaven?
   I'll find my way through night and day,
   'Cause I know I just can't stay here in heaven.

To Be With You

Words and Music by Eric Martin and David Grahame

Strum Pattern: 2
Pick Pattern: 4

1. Hold on, _____ lit-tle girl, _____ show me what he's
2. Build up _____ your _ con-fi-dence. so you can be on

done to you. Stand up, _____ lit-tle girl, _____ a bro-ken heart can't
top for once. Wake up, _____ who cares a-bout _ lit-tle boys that

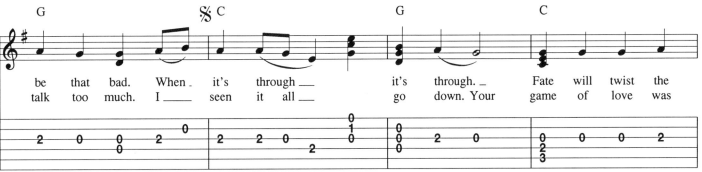

be that bad. When _ it's through _____ it's through. _ Fate will twist the
talk too much. I _____ seen it all _____ go down. Your game of love was

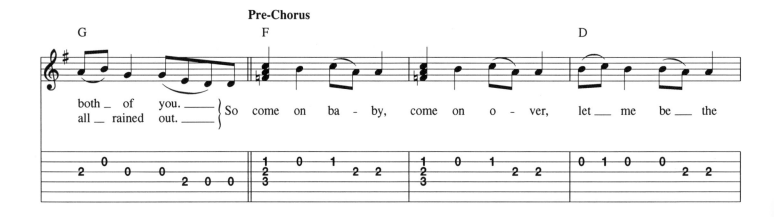

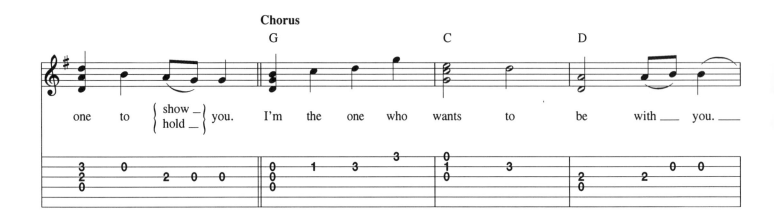

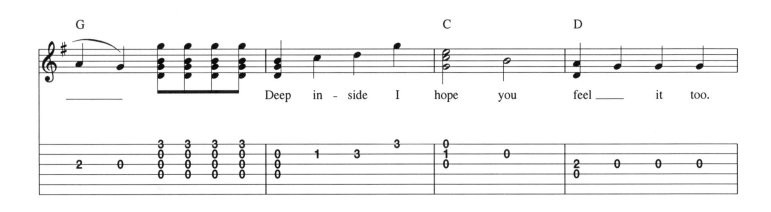

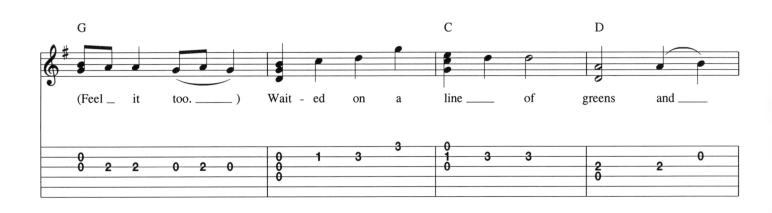

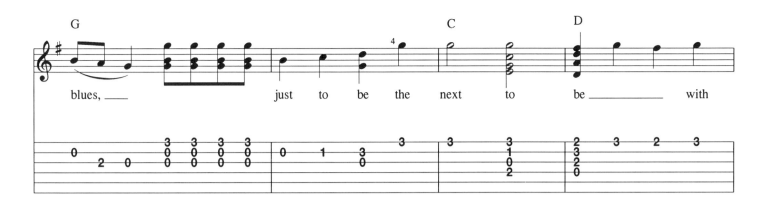

blues, _____   just to be the next to be _____ with

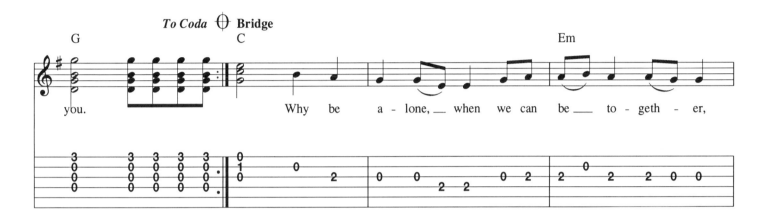

you.   Why be a - lone, __ when we can be __ to - geth - er,

ba - by?   You __ can make my life worth - while. __ I ____ can make you

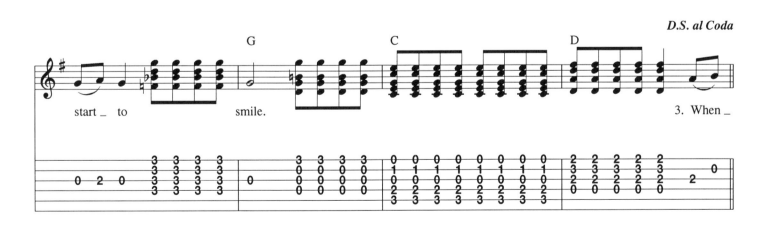

start _ to   smile.   3. When _

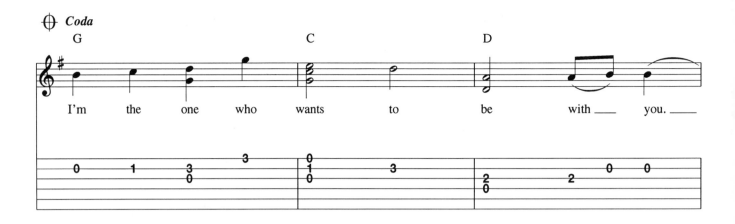

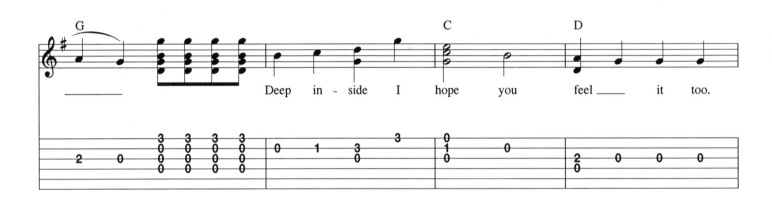

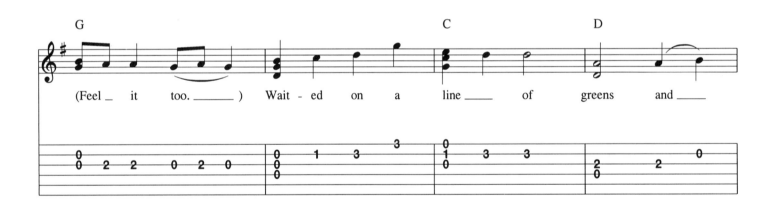

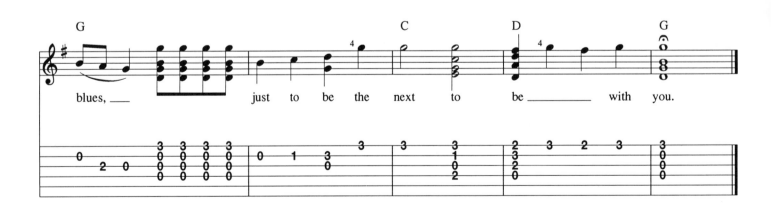

Wanted Dead Or Alive

Words and Music by Jon Bon Jovi and Richie Sambora

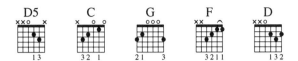

Strum Pattern: 1, 3
Pick Pattern: 2, 4

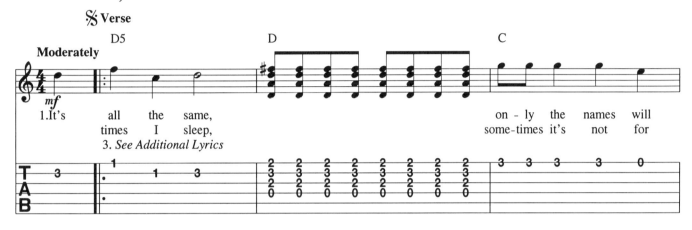

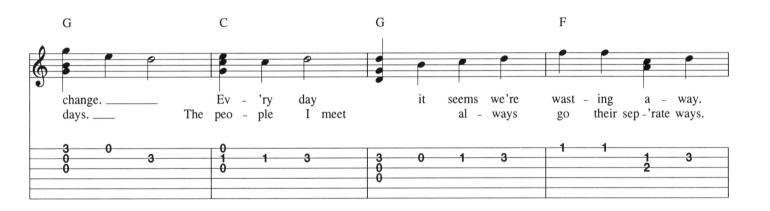

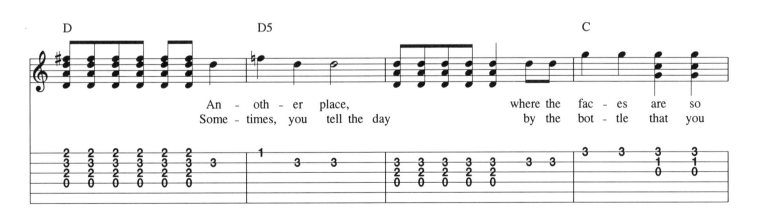

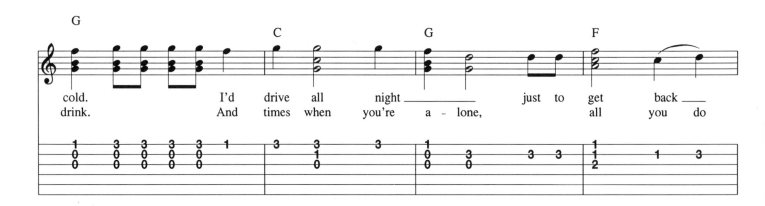

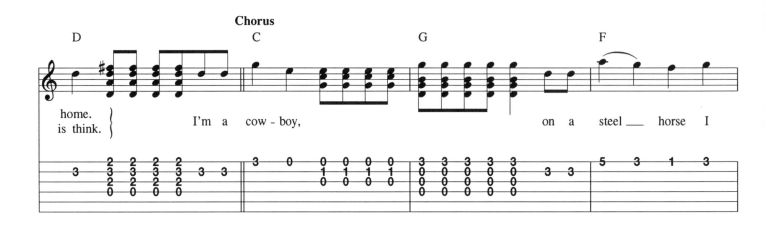

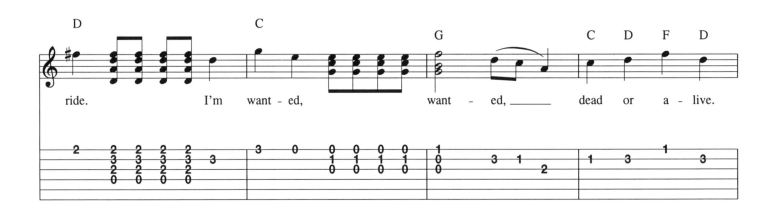

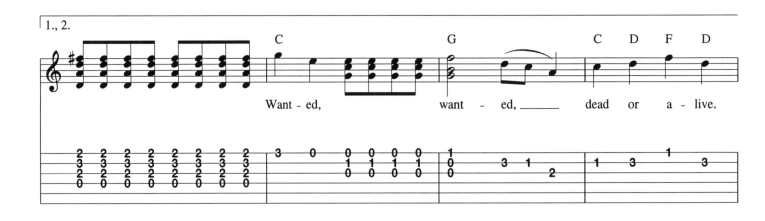

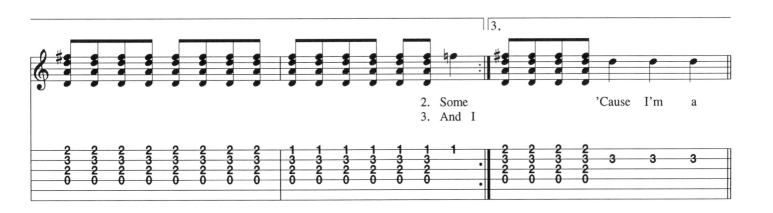

Outro

Additional Lyrics

3. And I walk these streets,
   A loaded six string on my back.
   I've seen a million faces, and I've rocked them all.
   I've been ev'rywhere, still I'm standing tall.
   I play for keeps, 'cause I might not make it back.

Wonderwall

Words and Music by Noel Gallagher

Strum Pattern: 3
Pick Pattern: 3

Intro

Moderately

play 4 times

1. To-day is gon-na be the day that they're gon-na throw it back to you, ___

by now you should've some-how re-al-ised what you got-ta do. ___

I don't be-lieve that an-y-bo-dy ___ feels the way I do ___ a-bout you now. ___

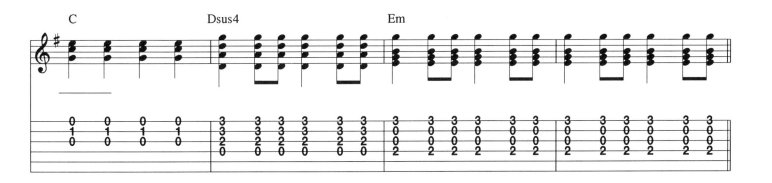

Verse

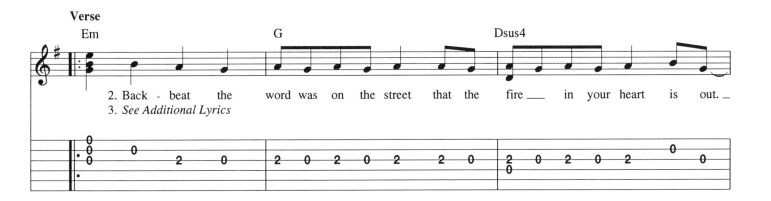

2. Back - beat the word was on the street that the fire ___ in your heart is out. ___
3. *See Additional Lyrics*

I'm sure you've heard it all be - fore but you

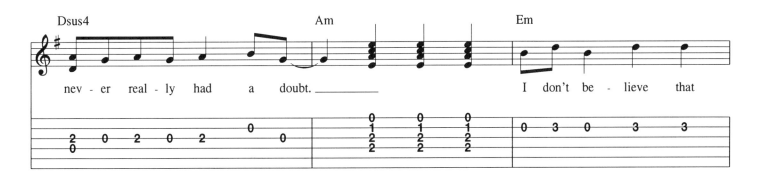

nev - er real - ly had a doubt. ___ I don't be - lieve that

an - y - bo - dy ___ feels the way I do ___ a - bout you now. ___

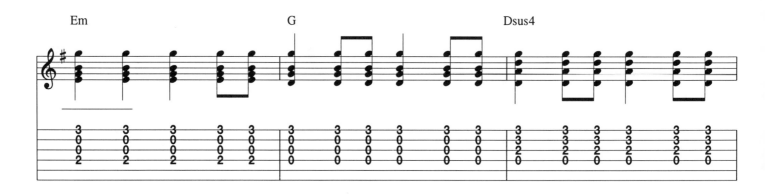

Pre-Chorus

And all ___ the roads ___ we have ___ to walk ___ are wind-
See Additional Lyrics

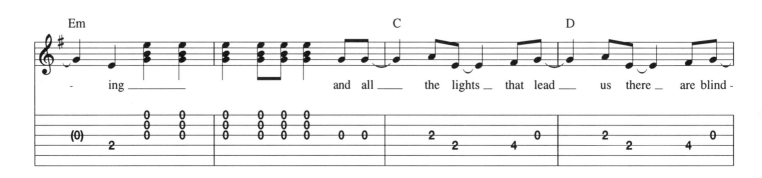

-ing ___ and all ___ the lights ___ that lead ___ us there ___ are blind-

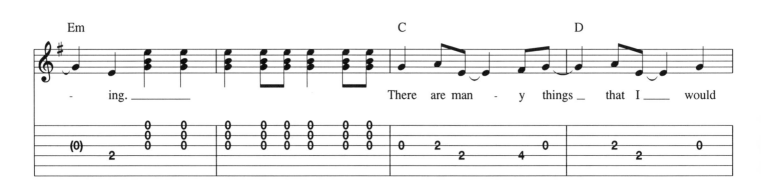

-ing. ___ There are man - y things ___ that I ___ would

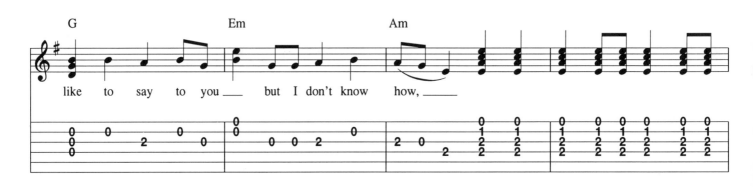

like to say to you ___ but I don't know how, ___

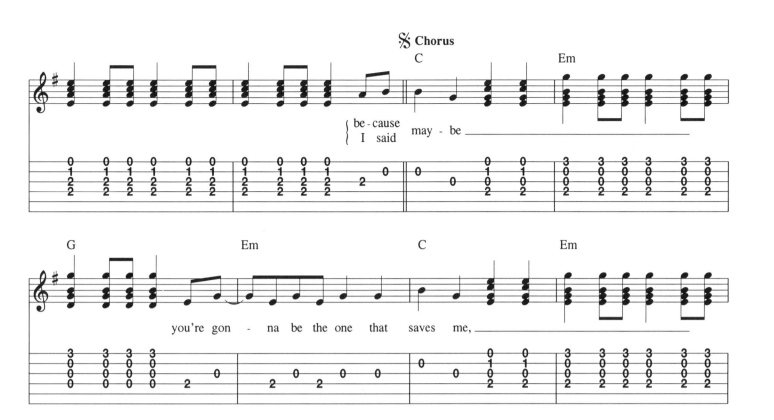

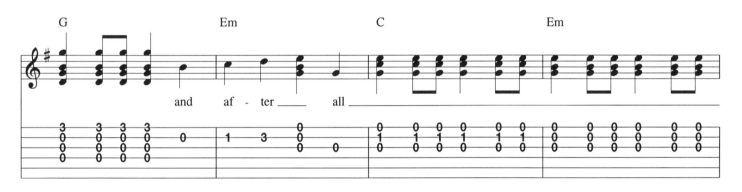

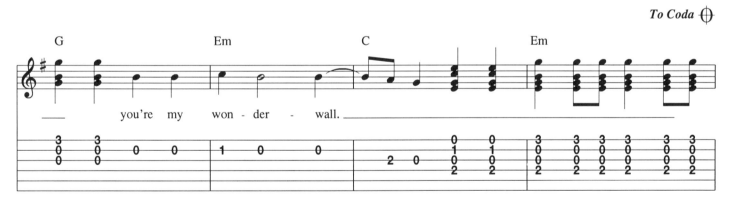

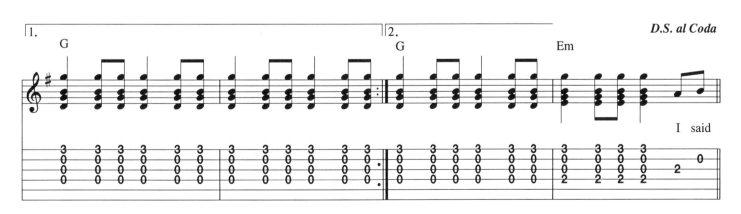

Additional Lyrics

3. Today was gonna be the day
   But they'll never throw it back to you.
   By now you should've somehow
   Realised what you're not to do.
   I don't believe that anybody
   Feels the way I do
   About you now.

Pre-Chorus And all the roads that lead you there were winding
   And all the lights that light the way are blinding.
   There are many things that I would like to say to you
   But I don't know how.

Yesterday

Words and Music by John Lennon and Paul McCartney

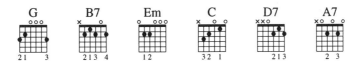

Strum Pattern: 2, 3
Pick Pattern: 2, 4

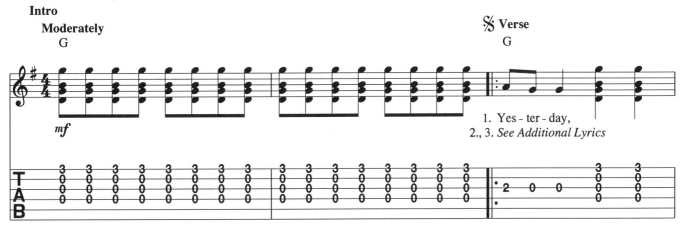

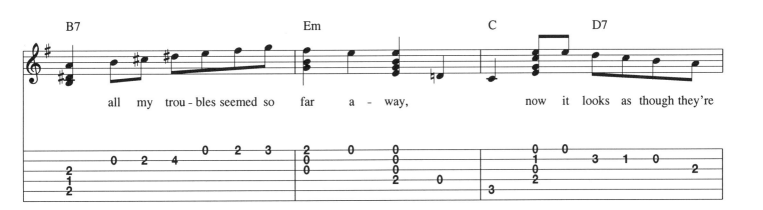

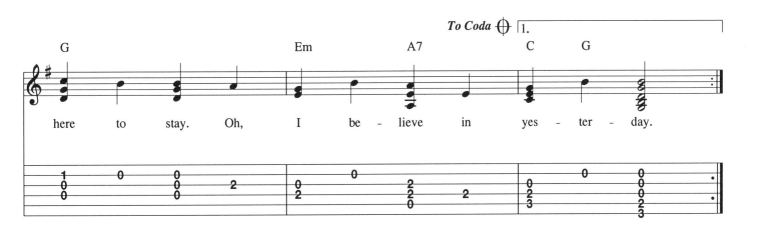

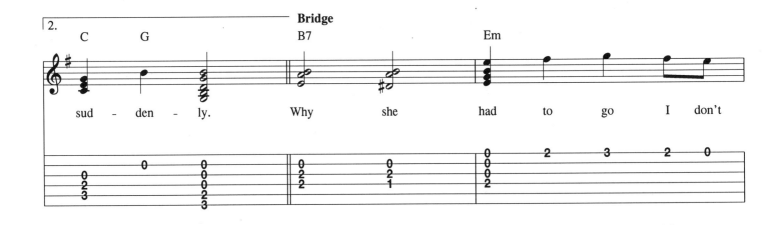

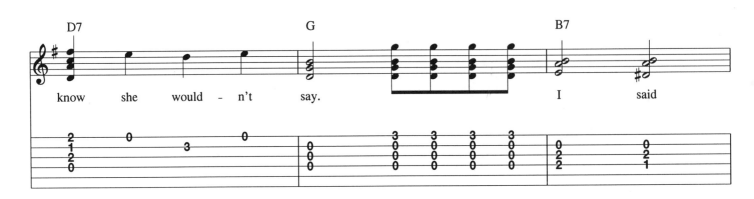

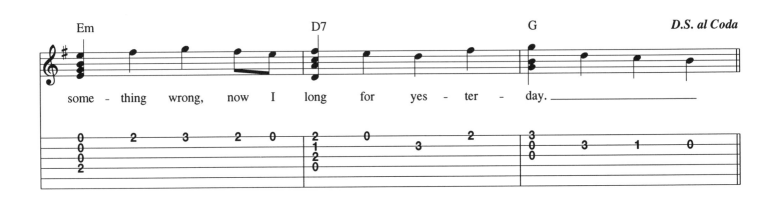

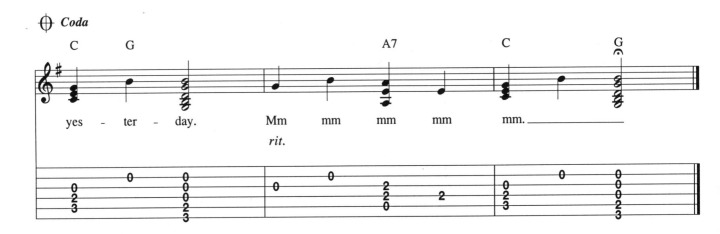

Additional Lyrics

2. Suddenly, I'm not half the man I used to be.
   There's a shadow hanging over me. Oh, yesterday came suddenly.

3. Yesterday, love was such an easy game to play.
   Now, I need a place to hide away. Oh, I believe in yesterday.